GREEN MANURING
FOR SOIL PRODUCTIVITY
IMPROVEMENT

by

O.P. Meelu
Yadvinder-Singh
Bijay-Singh

Department of Soils
Punjab Agricultural University
Ludhiana, India

FOOD AND AGRICULTURE ORGANIZATION OF THE UNITED NATIONS
Rome, 1994

M-53
ISBN 92-5-103515-6

Preface

Green manuring — a practice of ancient origin — is defined as the use of green plant material, grown *in situ* or cut and brought in for incorporation to improve soil productivity. The concept is distinct from, although having elements in common, with short- or long-duration cover-cropping and rotational ploughing-in of green crop residues such as mungbean. The species commonly used are of the *Leguminosae* with *Crotalaria juncea* (sunn hemp) and *Sesbania aculeata* (sesbania) being the most popular in India, and *Vicia* spp., *Trifolium* spp. and *Astragalus sinicus* in cooler climates.

Chapter 2 outlines the standard cultivations involved. A small starter-application of N may be beneficial on some soils, as also of P instead of applying it to the following rice crop. There is some flexibility in age at which green manure should be incorporated; 7 to 8 weeks, i.e. just before the onset of woodiness, is a guideline. The importance of thorough incorporation is stressed and various mechanical devices are mentioned; the most efficient, a tractor/disc-harrow system, however, is beyond the reach of most small farmers. An efficient but labour-intensive method involves traditional ploughing-in of sesbania in standing water and trampling the herbage into the paddy field. Time for decomposition before establishing the main crop is also an important consideration; evidence is variable but seems to suggest up to 8 weeks for rainfed conditions and up to 2 weeks for irrigated rice areas. In addition to the root-nodulating, N_2-fixing system of leguminous green manures, mention is made of *S. rostrata* that bears nodules on the stem. Another source of atmospheric N_2 is the floating fern *Azolla pinnata* which, in symbiosis with a N_2-fixing blue-green alga, is an efficient carrier of N to rice. Techniques for its multiplication and use in wetland rice are given. Perennial legumes such as *Gliricidia sepium* and *Leucaena leucocephala* grown separately in rows or on bunds provide another source of green manure from prunings taken five or six times a year.

Chapter 3 and Annex 2 report biomass and N content for various species from worldwide locations. Values for the former vary greatly within species and location, ranging from 2.9 to 9.9 t/ha dry-matter basis for annual species, and up to 80 t/ha/year fresh material for *Leucaena*. Yields of over 100 kg N/ha in the herbage are common in 60-day-old sesbania, but values exceeding 200 kg N/ha are reported from the Philippines, China and the USA. The proportion of plant N derived from the atmosphere can amount to 90 percent in *S. rostrata* and *S. cannabina*. *Azolla pinnata* contains 4-5 percent N on a dry-weight basis and can fix an average of 2 kg N/ha/day. Differences between the six *Azolla* spp. in ability to fix N_2 vary up to 8-fold according to season.

The fates of individual nutrients released from incorporated green manure are discussed in Chapter 4. Factors affecting the mineralization kinetics of N include N content of the herbage, C/N ratio and lignin content; release is retarded by high values of the last two, and accelerated by high temperatures and anaerobic conditions. Under waterlogged conditions the time of peak release is at least two weeks after incorporation. Mineralization of P re-cycled from the subsoil follows a similar process to that for N, except that no losses by volatilization occur. Other decomposition products exert a chelation effect on cations immobilizing P, thus increasing the net availability of soil P. Under waterlogged conditions green manuring increases availability of soil P to a greater extent at more extreme pH values than when near neutrality. Potassium and minor elements appear to be mobilized from the soil minerals by the action of CO_2 and organic acids released during decomposition. Similarly with trace elements such as Fe, Mn and Cu.

The decomposition products of green manures have a marked effect on soil biological, electro-chemical and physical properties. Bacterial and fungal populations are increased, and that of nematodes are decreased. Effect on pH is complex but tends towards the establishment of neutrality. Redox potential is reduced under waterlogged conditions, but electrical conductivity tends to increase. Physical conditions are improved primarily through the addition of organic matter and its decomposition products, e.g. polysaccharides, which confer a cementing action on soil particles thereby increasing the proportion of water-stable aggregates. Bulk density is reduced and consequently porosity increased, as is also water-holding capacity and infiltration rate. In addition to these soil-stabilizing effects, the growing crop dissipates the energy of rain drops and reduces liability to runoff of surface soil.

Green manuring brings about favourable changes in the physico-chemical properties of saline-sodic soils and is useful in their reclamation. Sesbania is a particularly valuable species since it withstands drought and waterlogging and is well-adapted to sodic soils. At high pH (over 8.5) the addition of gypsum may be necessary to ensure germination and high production of biomass. Both soil amendments are complementary, and enhance replacement of exchangeable Na by Ca in calcareous sodic soils. Green manuring itself increases rice yields on sodic soils.

Chapter 7 records the large amount of research on rice, particularly with sesbania and sunn hemp, done throughout the tropics. Yield increases exceeding 100 percent, i.e. 1.0 - 2.0 t/ha are commonly reported in India. Similar good responses to green-leaf manuring (GLM) occur using indigenous or planted perennial legumes such as *L. leucocephala, G. sepium, Tephrosia* spp. and *Aeschynomene americana*. Although crop land and growing time are not being occupied, GLM imposes heavier labour input. Intercropping rice with sesbania is feasible where a second crop follows. Short-duration pulse crops are useful green manures after harvest of the grains.

In general, recovery of N from green manure is similar to that from N fertilizer, values ranging from 25 to 50 percent. The most valuable comparative parameter is nitrogen fertilizer equivalent (NFE). A wide range of values are quoted – up to 150 kg N/ha – but more typically they lie between 50 and 100 kg N/ha. Responses to azolla are of the same order. A considerable amount of research is reported on the use of green manures in dryland cropping in the tropics and subtropics, e.g. maize, wheat and sorghum. Results tend to parallel those for rice but the practice is less widespread. Residual effects in terms of organic matter and N build-ups are reviewed, but no clear-cut findings emerge.

Chapter 8 exposes underlying constraints to the extended use of green manuring and emphasizes economic factors. Finally, a comprehensive list of suggested lines for future research and practical economic studies is presented.

Contents

List of figures

List of tables

Page

Chapter 1

Introduction

DEFINITIONS

Green manuring is an arable-farming practice in which undecomposed green plant material is incorporated into the soil in order to increase its immediate productivity. This material may either be obtained from quick-growing green-manure crops grown *in situ* or harvested elsewhere, usually from a perennial crop, and brought in. The species most commonly used are members of the *Leguminosae* (see Annex 1).

Green manuring should not be confused with **cover-cropping**, in which a crop, generally a legume of longer duration, is sown primarily to protect the soil from erosion, conserve moisture and to suppress weeds, while at the same time improving soil-N status and fertility in general. Neither should the practice be confused with the growing of legumes for harvesting in the **rotation**, which also contributes to soil fertility maintenance through the decay of the root system with its associated N_2-fixing nodules. In practice, however, it may be difficult to make a clear distinction among all three practices, particularly when whole-crop residues, e.g. of mungbean (*Vigna radiata*) are ploughed in.

Green manuring has been applied to a wide range of annual crops in various parts of the world, but it has been most successful when used in wetland rice cultivation in Asia.

HISTORICAL BACKGROUND

The practice of green manuring is as old as the art of manuring crops. Documented evidence on the value of green manures can be found as early as 500-400 BC in the writings of Varahamihira in India (Kadke 1965) and of Xenophon in Mediterranean civilizations (Smith *et al.* 1987). More than 2000 years ago Chinese farmers recognized that legumes increased production of the crops that followed (Pieters 1927), and the Romans recognized the soil-improving value of *Vicia faba* beans. In North America, green manuring has existed as a farming practice since the eighteenth century.

For centuries, therefore, farmers harvested low but consistent crop yields with little or no chemical fertilizer inputs. Replenishment of N and organic matter in cropped soils was obtained through organic and green manures.

POTENTIAL FOR GREEN MANURING

The increasing food to meet the requirement of fast-growing populations has led to intensive cropping with high-yielding varieties, particularly in India, resulting in increased demand for soil-nutrient supply on already over-exploited land, and application of fertilizers to keep crop yields high. The introduction in the last 25 years of improved varieties of rice and wheat, together with increased irrigation facilities and greater use of fertilizers and other inputs, has brought about the 'green revolution' and changed much of Asia from a region of food scarcity to one of food sufficiency. Of the total world rice output, more than 90 percent is produced in Asia, where it is increasing annually at the rate of 2.7 percent (IRRI 1986). From 1965 to 1980, some 24 percent of the increase in rice production in Asia was mainly attributed to the use of N fertilizers (Barker *et al.* 1985). Less attention has been paid to developing management techniques that maintain soil productivity, while reducing dependence on fertilizers. In this regard the importance of organic manures has been overlooked.

In recent years increasing fertilizer costs, and concern for sustainable soil productivity and ecological stability in relation to use of chemical fertilizers, have emerged as issues of vital concern. Furthermore, heavy reliance on chemical fertilizers tends to favour economically those farmers with large hectarage. These considerations have led to a renewed interest in organic manures such as farmyard manure, compost and green manures. The first two are limited in supply and have low and variable nutrient contents. The more readily available green manures, therefore constitute a valuable potential source of N and organic manure.

ADVANTAGES OF GREEN MANURING

In India, green-manure crops used to be grown without irrigation in fallow fields in the wet season. The benefit was obtained in the following dry-season crop. Under modern intensive cropping systems, however, a farmer cannot afford to allocate an entire crop season to a green-manure crop, and the need has arisen to establish a place for green manuring in the present-day intensive cropping systems. Recent studies have shown that up to 100 kg N/ha or more can be accumulated by *Sesbania aculeata*, a green-manure crop, in a 7- to 8-week fallow period available before transplanting of the wet-season rice crop (Beri and Meelu 1981; Bhardwaj and Dev 1985; Morris *et al.* 1989). Similar amounts of N addition through sesbania and sunn hemp have been reported from China (Bin 1983). In temperate climates also, winter green-manure crops such as milk vetch in China (Bin 1983) and legume cover crops in the United States (Smith *et al.* 1987) have been shown to accumulate well over 100 kg N/ha without interfering with the scheduling of summer grain crops.

Green manuring may also increase the availability of several other plant nutrients and micronutrients through its favourable impact on the physical, chemical and biological properties of the soil. Furthermore, green manures are a suitable means for minimizing losses of soil organic matter and reducing compaction and soil erosion, while still maintaining economic returns. When used as a supplement to chemical fertilizers, green manures may enhance their efficiency in increasing crop yields. The importance of green-manure crops in reclamation of salt-affected soils has also long been recognized.

The role of green manures in agricultural production should, therefore be viewed on a broad scale. With returning interest in green manuring, particularly in the light of the increasing costs of fertilizers, this report aims at presenting important research findings on green manuring for the improvement of soil productivity, with a view to its use by research workers, those engaged in planning and extension work, students and eventually farmers themselves. The material in this monograph is drawn mainly from the Indian experience.

Chapter 2

Green manuring practices

ECOLOGICAL BACKGROUND

Green manuring is practised in several ways. Typically, a green manure is grown in monoculture for various durations and incorporated into the same field. Alternatively, a green-manure crop may be grown as an intercrop or in mixed cropping. In addition, short-duration varieties of crops such as mungbean are grown for the dual purpose of grains and green manuring, the residues after picking the pods being used for green manuring the following crop. In the alley- or hedge-cropping system, food crops are grown in alleys formed between the hedge rows of leguminous trees or shrubs. These are periodically pruned during the crop-growing season to provide substantial amounts of organic matter and nitrogen when added to the soil.

An interesting and unique system is the green manuring of wetland rice using an aquatic fern *Azolla* spp. whose minute, bilobed leaves host in symbiosis a N_2-fixing blue-green alga *Anabaena azollae* (see section on *Azolla*).

Legumes used as green-manure crops can be grown on a wide range of soil types varying from sandy to clayey (Raheja 1952). Of the numerous species used as green manures, *Sesbania aculeata* (sesbania) and *Crotalaria juncea* (sunn hemp) are the most commonly grown and productive green manures in ordinary tropical soils. Vetches and clovers are the major winter green-manure crops used in temperate climates.

Evans (1990) reported that sesbania species may be annual herbs or shrubs, perennial shrubs or small trees. The majority are annual herbs from 1 to 4 m high with slightly or semi-woody stems. The ecological distribution of sesbania is diverse. They are generally found in zones that are semi-arid to sub-humid (wet-dry tropical) with annual rainfall between 500 and 2000 mm and are more commonly naturalized in regions that have alternating wet and dry periods than those with evenly distributed rainall. They often grow beside streams, lakes and swamps. They are well adapted to fluctuations in soil moisture, being tolerant of both drought and waterlogging. In general, they tolerate soils with high salt content and/or alkaline pH and some species are believed to tolerate acid soils.

Sesbania withstands saline and alkali conditions better than other green manures and pulses (Uppal 1955; Uppal *et al*. 1961; Abrol 1982). It also tolerates flooding and waterlogging (Vachhani and Murty 1964; Arunin *et al*. 1988; Morris *et al*. 1989) and is therefore more suitable for lowland rice. Sunn hemp, mungbean, cowpea and clusterbean, however, are more tolerant to drought (Vachhani and Murty 1964; Singh *et al*. 1981a).

TABLE 1
Seeding rate (kg/ha) of different green manure crops

Species	Seed rate	Reference
S. aculeata		
- normal soils	50-60	Chela & Gill (1973): Singh *et al.* (1981a), Meelu *et al.* (1992)
- salt-affected soils	60-70	Dargan *et al.* (1982), Ghai *et al.* (1988)
S. rostrata	30-40	Diekman & DeDatta (1990), Ventura & Watanabe (1991)
Cowpea	30-35	Singh *et al.* (1981a)
Clusterbean	50	Meelu *et al.* (1992), Singh *et al.* (1981a), Beri *et al.* (1989a)
Soybean	50	Meelu *et al.* (1992)
Mungbean/pigeonpea/Indigofera/lablab	30	Meelu *et al.* (1992)
Tephrosia purpurea	45	Krishna Rao (1957)

CULTIVATION PRACTICES

In order to maximize benefit from green manuring, an understanding of cultural practices is important. Those used mainly in tropical conditions are described below.

Number of Cultivations

In rainfed areas where a green-manure crop is raised in fallow fields during the rainy season, two cultivations are usually enough (Raheja 1952; Chela and Gill 1973). However, in the Philippines, the conventional method of land preparation for growing a green manure crop is one ploughing and one or two harrowings of the flooded soil (Ventura and Watanabe 1991). In irrigated areas in India, green manures can be grown in the summer season without preparatory tillage. In salt-affected soils, the land is usually ploughed two or three times followed by planking (levelling). If, however, the time for growing a green-manure crop is limited, its cultivation may be omitted (Dargan *et al.* 1982).

Method of Sowing

Green manures are usually broadcast (Raheja 1952; Chela and Gill 1973). One of three basic methods may be used:

□   over the ploughed field followed by planking to cover the seed with soil;
□   on a levelled field followed by incorporating the seed with harrow or cultivator and then planking;
□   on an uncultivated field after rains and mixed-in with a cultivator followed by planking.

Seed such as sesbania may be soaked overnight in water to hasten germination. A close contact between seed and soil in moist condition is necessary for satisfactory germination. In rainfed areas of eastern India, rice together with 15-20 kg/ha sesbania seed are dry-seeded by broadcasting (Garrity and Flinn 1988). For rainfed lowland rice in Thailand, Herrera *et al.* (1989) broadcast sesbania seeds and raked them lightly into the soil.

Seed can also be sown by manual drilling behind a plough in rows about 20-30 cm apart followed by planking, or by bullock/tractor-drawn seed drill (Chela and Gill 1973; Meelu *et al.* 1992). Arakeri and Patil (1957) and Tirol-padre and Ladha (1990) suggested that drilling was better than broadcasting.

Time of Sowing

Green manure is grown in the summer dry season for use in the wet season crop (Singh *et al.* 1982; Beri *et al.* 1989a, b; Ventura and Watanabe 1991; Meelu *et al.* 1992), or in the rainy season for the benefit of the dry-season crop (Becker *et al.* 1990; Anant Rao *et al.* 1957; Manguiat *et al.* 1989). There can be no rigid time schedule for sowing rainfed green-manure crops as the commencement of the monsoon rains varies from region to region. In northern India, rainfed green-manure crops are sown in early July or as early as possible after the break of the monsoon (Mirchandani and Khan, 1952). Under irrigated conditions, a green-manure crop can be sown from mid-April to mid-May depending upon the harvest of the dry-season crop. It may be concluded that a growing period for the green-manure crop of 6-8 weeks before transplanting/planting the main crop is necessary.

Seed Rate

A high seed rate is recommended for green manuring in order to delay development of woodiness. For sesbania and sunn hemp a seed rate of 50 kg/ha is normal. However, in salt-affected soils where germination is likely to be low, an even higher seed rate may be used. The seed rates used by different workers for different green manure crops in normal and salt-affected soils are given in Table 1.

Diekmann and De Datta (1990) found that *S. rostrata* at a seed rate of 40 kg/ha accumulated 114 kg N/ha compared with 100 kg N/ha with a rate of 50 kg/ha, in a 45-day growth period. (It is to be noted that scarification of *S. rostrata* seed is necessary, which may be a problem for farmers.) Becker *et al.* (1988), in a trial of vegetative propagation, observed that 30-cm stem cuttings (100 cuttings/m^2) of 8-week-old *S. rostrata* produced more biomass and N yield than 80 kg seed/ha or 20-cm cuttings.

Inoculation

Most leguminous crops can form root nodules and fix N_2 without prior inoculation with *Rhizobium*. In a field trial, Singh (1990) observed no significant effect of inoculation on nodulation and dry matter and N yield of sesbania. In regions where such a crop is introduced for the first time, however, there may be difficulty in obtaining nodulation without inoculation, which enhances the onset and number of effective nodules and hence the amount of N_2 fixed by a legume. In China, milk vetch was found to respond to inoculation (Chen 1988). Jia (1986) found that, during the first year of cultivation, inoculation of milk vetch seed with *Rhizobium* gave a four-fold increase in green-matter production. In Bangladesh, *Rhizobium* inoculation increased nodulation and dry-matter yield of sesbania (Subba Rao 1988). In Pakistan, Siddiqui *et al.* (1985) reported that inoculation increased the number of nodules/plant and height of sesbania only at low levels of P and K application. Gaur (1978) reported that *Rhizobium* inoculation increased the yield of sesbania by about 19 percent. Herridge and Brockwell (1988) reported that nodulation, shoot dry weight and N_2 fixation of soybean were markedly increased with inoculation. Bhardwaj (1974) considered that

TABLE 2
Effect of P application on biomass and N accumulation in green-manure crops

Green-manure crop	Available soil P (kg/ha)	Rate of fertilizer P (kg/ha)	Dry biomass (t/ha)		N accumulation (kg/ha)		Reference
			-P	+P	-P	+P	
Sunn hemp	0.036% (Total P)	39.2	27.7 (F)	31.9 (F)	-	-	Anant Rao *et al.* (1957)
Sunn hemp	60	7.3	13.2 (F)	13.6 (F)	-	-	Desai *et al.* (1957)
Cluster-bean	0.030% (Total P)	26.2	15.1 (F)	18.2 (F)	-	-	Shinde and Sen (1958)
Sunn hemp	-	-	6.1	7.7	-	-	Krishna Rao and Murthy (1962)
Sunn hemp	low	17.6	-	-	66	83	Singh (1961)
Cowpea	low	17.6	-	-	45	52	Singh (1961)
Milk vetch	-	-	20.9 (F)	31.5 (F)	-	-	Ku-Jung-Shen (1978a)
S. aculeata	4.5	13.1	4.0	4.2	88	105	Beri and Meelu (1981)
Sunn hemp	14.3	13.1	4.0	4.8	120	149	Sharma and Mittra (1988)
S. aculeata	14.3	13.1	3.4	3.7	87	98	Sharma and Mittra (1988)
S. aculeata	low	22.0	4.0	5.1	86	116	Herrera *et al.* (1989)
S. aculeata	11.0	26.2	8.0	9.6	117	142	Singh (1990)

F = Fresh matter

TABLE 3
Effect of P application and green manuring on rice yield

Reference	No. of expts.	P rate (kg/ha)	Rice yield (t/ha)		Percent increase
			P to rice	P to GM	
Sen & Rao (1953)	-	22	2.1	2.8	33
Panse *et al.* (1965)	10	11-30	1.9	2.0	6
	2	7-30	2.3	2.3	0
Beri & Meelu (1981)	2	13	4.2	4.9	17
Herrera *et al.* (1989)	1	22	2.2	2.8	25
Sharma & Mittra (1988)	2	13	3.4	3.7	9
Helepyati & Sheelavantar (1991)	2	22	4.9	5.6	14

Rhizobium was abundantly distributed in salt-affected soils of India as good nodulation of sesbania plants was noted. However, a considerable number of the nodules were ineffective. Application of gypsum for soil reclamation stimulated growth and multiplication of *Rhizobium* which in turn gave a better start to the leguminous crops (National Academy of Sciences 1979).

The special cases of stem-nodulating legumes and the use of Azolla are discussed in the sections on stem-nodulating legumes and *Azolla*, respectively.

Fertilizer Application

Leguminous green manures do not usually require supplemental N. In N-deficient soils, however, a starter dose of 15-25 kg N/ha is beneficial. In a soil low in organic carbon (0.39 percent), Sharma and Mittra (1988) observed an increase in N-accumulation of 30 kg N/ha in sunn hemp and 23 kg N/ha in sesbania, with the application of a starter dose of 15 kg N/ha. Chapman and Myers (1987) found that at flowering, a starter dose of 25 kg N/ha increased N in the tops by about 10 percent in sesbania and green gram, and by about 30 percent in soybean, but at maturity N-yield was unaffected by N application. In salt-affected soils, a starter dose of 20 kg N/ha is recommended (Dargan *et al*. 1982). Ku-Jung-Shen (1978a) suggested that about 20 kg N/ha applied in early spring will speed-up the growth of milk vetch. In both greenhouse and field studies, Becker *et al*. (1991) showed an increase in N yields of 2 kg for every kg of N (upto 30 kg N/ha) applied to *S. rostrata*. Sanginga *et al*. (1988b) found that application of 40 kg N/ha proved beneficial to satisfy the plant needs during the early growth stage of *L. leucocaphala*.

Leguminous plants are well able to utilize soil P. However, from the data recorded by several authors in Table 2, it appears that, on P-deficient soils, green manures do respond to added P in terms of N-accumulation, but not of biomass on high-P soils.

In the Philippines, Meelu and Morris (1988) obtained a N-accumulation of 199 kg/ha in sesbania without P application on soils testing high in available P. Vachhani and Murty (1964) reported that 13 kg P/ha applied to mungbean for green manuring did not increase the fresh-matter yield. Gu and Wen (1981) reported that, if the available P were below 15 ppm in acid and neutral soils and below 10 ppm in calcareous soils, then P-fertilizer application would be markedly effective. Good results from potassium and molybdenum applications to milk vetch were also obtained. Ishikawa (1988) reported that normally no fertilizer was needed for milk-vetch production in Japan; however, 7-14 kg P/ha applied as superphosphate significantly increased fresh-matter yield. In Nigeria, Sanginga *et al*. (1988a) found that nodulation, total N and shoot dry weight of *L. Leucocephala* were markedly increased by applying 40 kg P/ha.

The effects of P-application to green manure on succeeding rice yields are given in Table 3. This shows that P application to the green manure gave higher rice yields than application directly to the rice, 6-33 percent higher rice yields being obtained by various workers. On the other hand, Vachhani and Murty (1964) and Panse *et al*. (1965) in 2 out of 12 experiments found no beneficial effect of P application to green manure on the yield of the succeeding rice crop.

The response of succeeding crops to green manuring is discussed in greater depth in Chapter 7, but it is pointed out that in view of the well-established residual effects of particularly P-fertilizers there is the danger of confounding their effects as between application to one or the other, or to both crops. This is an important issue since farmers usually apply fertilizer to every crop in the rotation.

It is concluded that further investigation is needed into the N- and P-fertilizing of leguminous green-manure crops grown in crop rotations, particularly those including highly-fertilizer-responsive varieties. Meanwhile, evidence suggests that, where rice does respond to applied P, it should preferably be applied to the preceding green-manure crop.

Irrigation

Dry matter and N yields of green-manure crops are affected by soil moisture supply, but their deep rooting conveys an advantage over other non-leguminous crops under conditions of soil-moisture stress. Singh and Lamba (1971) recommended that cowpeas should be irrigated when the available water in the 180-cm profile was depleted to 35 percent. Gaul *et al.* (1976) reported that during summer in northern India, about 600-650 mm of irrigation water was required for raising a 74-day-old green-manure crop of sesbania on sodic soils. Singh *et al.* (1981a) studied water expense and water-use efficiency of sesbania, cowpea and clusterbean green-manure crops. The water-use efficiency was highest for cowpea under all irrigation schedules. Total water expense of 7-week-old green manures was 36-38 cm under favourable irrigation schedules (IW/PAN-E = 1.0). From China, Gu and Wen (1981) reported that for optimum yield of milk vetch, surface moisture (0-10 cm) should be maintained at about 70 percent of water-holding capacity till winter in order to stimulate growth of the root system. Further studies are necessary in this area of research with different species of green manure to discover the most efficient water-users.

Age at Incorporation

The age at which a green-manure crop should be ploughed-in is important for maximum benefit. In India, Mirchandani and Khan (1952) concluded that a green-manure crop should be turned into the soil at the point of flowering, i.e. about 8 weeks from sowing in most crops. Chela and Gill (1973) considered that sesbania attained maximum growth about 8 weeks after sowing, sunn hemp was ready for ploughing-in 60-70 days after sowing when flowering began all over the crop, and clusterbean reached flowering 7 to 8 weeks after sowing. Panse *et al.* (1965) reported a crop of 7- to 8-week old sunn hemp/sesbania produced the best responses with rice and wheat. Vachhani and Murty (1964) found that 8-week-old sesbania was tender and succulent and should be turned-in at the time of transplanting of rice for maximum response.

Khan and Mathur (1957) studied the effect of incorporating sunn hemp at 4, 6, 8 and 10 weeks after sowing on the yield of wheat, and found that incorporation 8 weeks after sowing gave maximum yield. Anant Rao *et al.* (1957) studied the effect of turning-in sunn hemp after 28, 35, 49, 56 and 72 days growth and found that 48 and 56 days growth was best for the following crop of wheat. Below 35 days there was insufficient biomass and plants were too woody at 72 days. Bhardwaj (1982) found that incorporating sesbania at 45, 55 and 65 days gave similar rice yields. Kolar and Grewal (1988) also found that turning-in sesbania, cowpea and sunn hemp at 40, 50 and 60 days each gave comparable rice yields.

Dargan *et al*. (1982) recommended incorporating sesbania at 7-9 weeks in salt-affected soils. Chandanani (1958) turned-in sunn hemp and clusterbean green manure for wheat after 7 to 8 weeks, and after 6 weeks when grown in alternate rows in maize. Singh (1961) investigating six green manures for wheat, turned them in after 7 weeks.

Review of the above work indicates that a green-manure crop may be incorporated at 7 to 8 weeks, which roughly coincides with the flowering/maximum growth stage of most green-manure crops.

Method of Incorporation

Proper incorporation of the green manure into soil containing sufficient moisture is important for rapid decomposition. Raheja (1952) reported that green-manure crops as high as 2 m can be readily buried by a soil-inverting plough, after the standing crop has been planked down.

The soil-inverting plough is run in the direction the crop has been laid flat in the field and again planked to compact the soil. Standard tractor-drawn disc-harrows can also be used. In the Philippines, Meelu *et al*. (1992) used a power-tiller-drawn mouldboard plough for *in situ* incorporation of eight 60-day-old green-manure crops. To help cut and incorporate a green-manure crop, the IRRI developed an attachment of ring-knives to the cage wheels of a power-tiller-drawn mouldboard plough. A local animal-drawn implement used by farmers in the Philippines has also shown promise for green-manure incorporation. The implement flattens a sesbania crop on the first pass while five sharp blades slice the branches. On the second pass at right angles, plant stems are cut into 25-cm sections and driven down into the mud; conventional ploughing and harrowing follow with no additional effort (Garrity and Flinn 1988).

In the rainfed areas of eastern India where rice and sesbania seeds are broadcast dry, the green-manure crop is incorporated by an operation known as *beushenning*. The field is ploughed and cross-ploughed in standing water after 4-6 weeks and the sesbania plants are trampled into the mud. This operation also thins the young rice crop and controls weeds.

Depth of Incorporation

The depth of incorporation influences the susceptibility of the green-manure-N to loss, and thus determines the efficiency of its use by the crop.

In Indonesia, Staker (1958) reported an increase in rice yield with incorporation of green manure rather than its surface application. From a three-year study, Williams and Finfrock (1962) showed that rice responded significantly better to deep (10-15 cm) incorporation of vetch green manure than to shallow incorporation. Oxidation conditions were probably maintained for a longer period at the shallower depths. As with fertilizer N, deep placement of green-manure-N reduces ammonia volatilization by minimizing the denitrification process before flooding, and thereby retains ammonium-N in the soil.

A green-manure crop should, therefore, be completely incorporated into the soil for full effectiveness, but in practice this may be difficult to accomplish.

Interval Between Incorporation and Crop Establishment

The interval between turning-in the green-manure crop must accommodate with the transplanting/sowing of the succeeding crop, particularly under intensive cropping where time available for growing a green-manure crop is relatively short. Hence the rate at which green manures decompose and mineralize in both upland and wetland ecosystems is important. Meelu *et al.* (1992) studied the response of rice to eight tropical green-manure crops and found that succulence and tissue-N, which were expected to be related to decomposition rate, were determined more by plant age than by species.

In rainfed areas, green manure is generally grown in the rainy season (early July in northern India) for the benefit of a dry-season crop. Green manure at about 8 weeks old is turned-under at the end of August before the monsoon ends. Wheat is sown at the end of October, giving a decomposition period of about two months. Khan and Mathur (1957) studied the effect of (a) age at incorporation (4 to 10 weeks) of sunn hemp and (b) time-interval between burial and sowing of a succeeding wheat crop. They found that 8 weeks was the correct timing for both periods and made optimum use of plant nutrients. Mirchandani and Khan (1952) also found that a two-months interval for sunn hemp green manuring gave the best results. Anant Rao *et al.* (1957) used an interval of 50-60 days between incorporating 49- to 56-day-old sunn hemp green manure and sowing wheat. Singh and Sinha (1964) applied green matter in early September and allowed it to decompose in the soil until sowing wheat in mid-November.

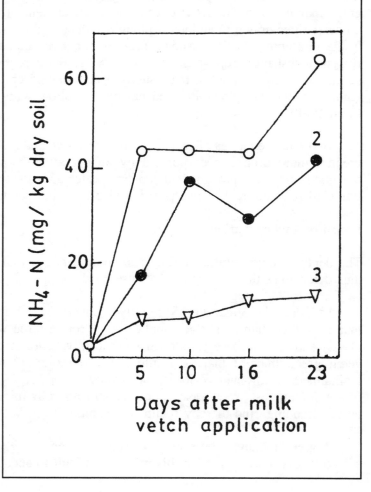

FIGURE 1

Changes in ammonium-N concentration in the soil with time of flooding after incorporation of milk vetch green manure

1 = simultaneous flooding and milk vetch incorporation
2 = flooding 5 days after milk vetch incorporation
3 = flooding 10 days after milk vetch incorporation

TABLE 4

Effect of interval between incorporation of green manure and rice transplanting on rice yield

Decomposition period (days)	Rice grain yield (t/ha)				
	Vachhani & Murty (1964)	Bhardwaj (1982)	Ghai *et al.* (1988)	Beri *et al.* (1989b)	Herrera *et al.* (1989)
0-1	3.2	5.9	5.9	6.2	2.4
5-7	-	-	6.1	5.3	-
10	-	5.7	6.1	-	2.7*
4-15	-	-	5.4	4.8	-
20	-	4.4	-	-	2.8
28	3.0	-	-	-	-
56	2.8	-	-	-	-

* 10 to 14-day decomposition period

In irrigated areas under intensive cropping in India, only about 8 weeks are available for growing a green-manure crop after the harvest of a dry-season crop and transplanting/sowing of a succeeding wet-season crop; thus a long decomposition period is not feasible. Results of experiments have shown that long decomposition periods for green manure are not necessary before rice transplanting. Adequate moisture content in the soil and high temperature enhances the rapidity of mineralization, and longer aerobic decomposition may result in N loss on flooding at rice transplanting. Ishikawa (1963) incorporated milk vetch green manure and flooded the soil simultaneously or up to 10 days later. He found that ammonium-N progressively decreased with delay in flooding after incorporation (Figure 1, Ishikawa 1963).

Higher yields of rice tend to be obtained by incorporating green manure up to ten days before transplanting rice compared with after longer periods, as reported by several authors in Table 4. The reasons for low efficiency of green manure when incorporated for a longer period before transplanting, could be the loss of green-manure-N by release during aerobic decomposition through NH_3-volatilization, nitrification-denitrification and leaching upon flooding (Chapman and Myers 1987). However, on a sodic soil Swarup (1987) reported that a 7-day decomposition period under flooded conditions for sesbania green manure gave significantly higher rice yields than simultaneous incorporation and transplanting of rice. This is because the nitrification process is slower in sodic soils.

Yamazaki (1959) reported that in well-drained fields where active nitrification occurred, rice yields of late-flooded plots (45 days after incorporating milk vetch) were less than the yields of early-flooded plots (20 days). On the other hand, in a poorly-drained field with possibly inactive nitrification, rice yield remained uninfluenced by timing of flooding. Williams and Finfrock (1962) confirmed that under conditions favourable to nitrification, the shorter the period before flooding the greater was the effectiveness of green manure. Nevertheless, drainage is still important for plant growth and rice production inspite of the loss of N it may cause.

However, Ishikawa (1988) stated that, in Japan, a suitable flooding time is one week after milk vetch incorporation. This reduces the effect of developing organic acids and the loss of N. With excess quantities of milk vetch application, rice-growth injuries caused by organic acids and excess N are reduced by delayed flooding. Wen (1984) preferred to incorporate green manure about 15 days before transplanting rice. This period eliminated possible damage from the decomposition products of the green manure. In Thailand, Herrera *et al*. (1989) working on acid, low-humic gley soils, suggested a delay of over one week before transplanting rice (Table 4). In Cameroon, Roy *et al*. (1988) suggested that sesbania and sunn hemp green manures should be incorporated about 2 weeks before transplanting rice.

Within the time available for growing a green manure and establishing the crop to be benefitted, three considerations arise: (1) need to maximize the quantity of green-manure material, (2) need to minimize loss of N after incorporation, (3) need to minimize toxic effects in a rice crop under waterlogged conditions. Evidence presented tends to suggest that in rainfed areas in northern India a period of 6-8 weeks is satisfactory, but that in lowland rice cultivation a shorter period of up to two weeks should be adopted.

SUB-TROPICAL GREEN-MANURING PRACTICES

Milk vetch (*Astragalus sinicus*) is the main green-manure crop used in China and Japan. It requires a well-drained soil and a cool climate. Seeds germinate at 4-5°C and the optimum growth temperature is 15-20°C. The optimum soil-water content is 60-75 percent of field capacity; plants may die if it falls below 40 percent. In China, a seed rate of 45-75 kg/ha is used (Garrity and Flinn 1988). When milk vetch is sown under a rice canopy, the seed rate is 22.5-37.5 kg/ha (Liu 1988). Seeds are broadcast in the field before late rice is harvested in mid-November (Chen 1988). Sowing time is mid-August to early September in northern Japan and early September to early October in warmer districts. In the following April, plants elongate rapidly, and reach full bloom in mid May. Ishikawa (1963) found that fresh weight ranged from 23 t/ha at the beginning of flowering to 47 t/ha at full bloom. Flowering appears to be the most suitable time to turn-in milk vetch.

Westcott and Mikkelson (1988) reported that in the United States, purple vetch or common vetch and occasionally bur clover are the species most commonly used for rice. Seed rate varies widely, depending upon the seed size, ranging from 6-17 kg/ha for clovers to 34-90 kg/ha for vetches. In California, rice fields are seeded before harvest with vetch by aeroplane. Winter rains provide moisture for growth and the green manure is incorporated in the spring as part of seed-bed preparation. Vetch is usually disked or rolled flat before ploughing to incorporate the above-ground material. Crimson clover is the most widely-used green-manure crop in south-east United States. In mid-September, inoculated seeds are broadcast into standing maize (Smith *et al*. 1987).

STEM-NODULATING LEGUMES

Nodules capable of fixing atmospheric N_2 are generally present on the roots of all legume species, but a few belonging to the genera: *Sesbania*, *Neptunia* and *Aeschynomene*, also produce nodules on the stem. Among these, *S. rostrata* and *A. afraspera* have received most attention because of the extensive nature of stem nodulation. Stem nodulating legumes can grow in upland or lowland (flooded) conditions (Ventura and Watanabe 1991), temporarily waterlogged soils, in swamps, marshes on riverbanks, or in the littoral region of freshwater lakes and rivers (Allen and Allen 1981). In the early growth stages the contribution of root nodules to plant is more than that of stem nodules which appear between 20 and 30 days after germination and suppress the root nodulation. Thereafter, the major contribution is from the stem nodules (Ladha *et al.* 1992). The nodulation sites are either epidermal (as in *S. rostrata*) or subepidermal (as in *A. crassicaulis*). When infected by a specific *Rhizobium* strain, tissues at these sites proliferate into stem nodules (Dreyfus *et al.* 1984).

In root-nodulating legumes, competition between native strains of *Rhizobium* and inoculated efficient strains, may result in nodules being formed by inefficient native strains that fix little or no N_2. In stem-nodulating plants competition from native strains may be low or non-existent. When *S. rostrata* was spray-inoculated with the antibiotic-resistant *Rhizobium* strain ORS 571, all nodules produced were due to the applied inoculum.

S. rostrata nodulates freely in most soils without inoculation. If the legume is being grown for the first time in an area, inoculation may be necessary. A practical method is to collect nodules from the stems of growing *S. rostrata*, crush them, mix them with water and filter. This solution can be sprayed on the stem and base of the growing plants (Ventura and Watanabe 1991). Stem inoculation by spraying appropriate rhizobia on stems of 2- to 7-week old plants has been proved useful for high biological N_2 fixation (Alazard and Duhoux 1987; Ladha *et al.* 1989). Shoots can be sprayed with suspension containing about 10^8 bacteria/ml using either a liquid culture of rhizobia, a colloidal suspension obtained by mixing trapped rhizobia in a phosphate buffer or a suspension of crushed stem nodules with water and passed through a filter (Rinaudo *et al.* 1988). The formation of stem nodules becomes macroscopically visible within 5 to 7 days after inoculation and the nodules reach their full size in 15 to 20 days. Rain water can wash the epiphytically growing rhizobia down the stems or soil splash due to rain may bring rhizobia to lower stem and thereby infect nodulation sites (Ladha *et al.* 1992).

Most stem nodulating legumes are tropical plants and, therefore, need relatively high temperature, more solar radiation and humidity for optimum growth and high N_2-fixing activity and N yield. Humidity enhances primordial development and increases the success of inoculation in stem-nodulating legumes (Becker *et al.* 1990, Ladha *et al.* 1992). Becker *et al.* (1991) showed that application of mineral P and K fertilizers stimulated nodulation and nitrogenase activity of *S. rostrata* and *A. afraspera* and increased N yield by 40 percent. Recent studies showed that *S. rostrata* performs satisfactorily on acid (Salam *et al.* 1989) and saline soils (Hansen and Munns 1985; Arunin *et al.* 1988).

S. rostrata have been found to be highly sensitive to photo period (Visperes *et al.* 1987; Palaniappan and Srinivasulu 1990). *A. afraspera* seems to be considerably less photoperiod sensitive (Becker *et al.* 1990). Ventura and Watanabe (1991) reported that because of its photosensitivity, it is not advisable to use *S. rostrata* during the short day months (October-February). During this period flowering is triggered and usually fast vegetative growth gives way to slow growth and seed production. However, *A. afraspera* is less sensitive to photoperiod than *S. rostrata* and performs better for green manure production during short day period (Becker *et al.* 1990).

Another important feature of stem-nodulation is its tolerance of high levels of substrate N. In hydroponic experiments Dreyfus and Dommergues (1980) studied the effect of a concentration of 3 mM NH_4NO_3 on nodulation and N_2 fixation by *S. rostrata*. Root

TABLE 5
Effect of inoculation on nodulation, dry matter and N yield of *S. rostrata*

Reference	Inoculation	Number of nodules per plant	Dry matter per plant (g)	Total N per plant (mg)
Ladha *et al.* (1989)	-	17	5.8	116
	+	78	8.4	176
Kulasooriya & Samarakoon (1990)	-	120*	4.3	45
	+	190*	6.2	82

* nodule dry weight per plant (mg)

nodulation and associated N_2-fixing activity were signficantly reduced, but nodulation and N_2 fixation by stem nodules were increased. Similar results were obtained by Becker et al. (1986) in *A. afraspera*. Saint Macary *et al.* (1985) observed that in water-logged conditions root nodulation of *S. rostrata* was poor and N_2-fixation activity was mainly due to stem nodules. Ladha *et al.* (1989) found that soil + seed + stem inoculation gave significantly more nodules (stem and roots) and higher biomass than the uninoculated control (Table 5). Root- and stem-inoculated plants produced the highest plant dry weights. Plants with uninoculated stems did not develop stem nodules. In Sri Lanka, Kulasooriya and Samarakoon (1990) reported that stem-inoculation of *S. rostrata* increased weight per plant by 45 percent and N-yield by 80 percent. Although the efficacy of stem-inoculation of *S. rostrata* has been well documented, its practicality and economics at farm level have yet to be shown.

Using ^{15}N dilution technique, Pareek *et al.* (1990) reported that the contribution of N from N_2 by well-nodulated 45-55 day old *S. rostrata* plants was about 70 percent and increased further to more than 90 percent at 65 days. The N accumulation potential of stem nodulating legumes under flooded conditions ranges from 41 kg N/ha in *A. indica* (Crozat and Sangchyo-sawat 1985) to more than 200 kg N/ha in *S. rostrata* (Alazard and Becker 1987; Becker *et al.* 1990; Rinaudo *et al.* 1983).

AZOLLA

Azolla is an aquatic fern that lives symbiotically with N_2 fixing blue green algae *Anabaena azollae*. The delicate fern provides nutrients and a protective leaf cavity for the anabaena, which in turn provides N for the fern. Worldwide, distribution of azolla is represented by six recognizable species: *A. filiculoides, A. caroliniana, A. mexicana, A. microphylla, A. nilotica* and *A. pinnata*. Their taxonomies are based on vegetative and reproductive structures. Azolla has been used as green manure for rice in Vietnam, China, Japan, Philippines, Thailand, Sri Lanka, India, Pakistan, Brazil and the United States. Azolla is grown as a monocrop or as an intercrop for green manuring in rice. As a green manure, azolla can be either grown in the flooded fallow fields and incorporated in the soil before transplanting, or multiplied in multiplication beds and used as green manure. As an intercrop, it is inoculated after rice transplanting and incorporated after about four weeks.

Environmental Requirements of Azolla

Water: Water is the most important single factor affecting azolla cultivation. Azolla can live on a moist soil surface but it multiplies best when floating on shallow fresh water with near neutral pH. Cultivation on a field scale, therefore, requires a constant dependable source of water of moderate temperature. Water control provides the best management tool for avoiding injury due to high or low temperature. A fairly shallow depth of water, 2.5-5.0 cm, is most suitable for azolla growth (Lumpkin 1987; Ventura and Watanabe 1991). This depth of water enables azolla roots to come into contact with the soil to absorb plant nutrients. A multiplication technique of azolla (*A. pinnata*) developed at the Central Rice Research Institute, Cuttack, India (Pande 1978) involves standing water of 5-10 cm.

To maintain azolla during the off-season, special nurseries are required to protect the culture from death or injury caused by extremes of cold or heat during overwintering and oversummering. When winters are severe, hot spring water or warm water from factories is useful for the overwintering of azolla (Ye and Wu 1964). During oversummering, the culture has to be kept at low temperature. It is suggested that the seed area should be kept near the trees to provide shade.

Recently, *A. caroliniana* and *A. filiculoides* have been successfully grown on the moist soil surface without the water layer, and these can tolerate low light intensity and resist rotting. These characteristics enable azolla to survive throughout the summer under the rice canopy. The moist soil cultivation of *A. caroliniana* and *A. filiculoides* is a useful new development in growing azolla and it is a technical improvement over water cultivation (Liu 1987). This method should prove useful in tropical Asian countries.

Temperature: Azolla can be severely affected by temperatures that are too high or too low. The optimum temperature for most azolla species is within the range of 20 to 35°C (Lumpkin 1987; Pande 1978). *A. filiculoides* and *A. microphylla*, *A. caroliniana* and *A. rubra* (Japonica) are quite tolerant of low temperatures, while *A. mexicana*, *A. microphylla*, *A. caroliniana*, *A. nilotica* and certain varieties of *A. pinnata* can tolerate high summer temperatures.

Light: The maximum growth rate of azolla has been reported at 25-50 percent of the full sunlight (Talley and Rains 1980b). As an intercrop under rice, the growth rate of azolla will decline when developing rice canopy reduces light quantity and quality below that necessary to ensure maximum growth rate (Lumpkin 1987). Day length is another important aspect of light. Growth rate has been shown to correlate positively to day length (Lumpkin and Bartholomew 1986).

Management Practices for Field Cultivation of Azolla

Azolla is mostly propagated vegetatively. A permanent propagation pond (or nursery) is needed for steady supply of the fern. The size of the pond will depend on the farmers' needs. Fields should be thoroughly tilled and properly levelled to kill competing plants and algae, and to obtain a uniform water depth. To begin ponds or fields must be inoculated with azolla. In the Philippines, Ventura and Watanabe (1991) used an inoculation rate of 0.2 to 0.3 kg fresh weight/m^2. In 10 to 15 days, the entire pond is expected to be fully covered producing fresh azolla weight from 1.2 to 2.0 kg/m^2. Once the azolla propagation plot is fully covered, a portion of the azolla biomass may be harvested periodically to maintain an azolla population of 1.2-2.0 kg/m^2 while also maintaining its high N and low lignin content. In rice fields, azolla doubles its weight in 3 to 5 days. A fully covered 1 ha plot of azolla weighs 12-20 t/ha and contains 30-50 kg N/ha. Pande (1978) divided the field into subplots of 50-100 m^2 to avoid accumulation leading to decreased growth and used 100 to 400 g/m^2 fresh azolla for inoculation on seeding. The green mass of azolla should be harvested on the formation of a layer after one week to avoid decomposition.

Another method of multiplying azolla in rice fields is setting aside 1000 m^2 enclosed with temporary bunds, and then putting 200-300 kg fresh azolla in it. When the 1000 m^2 area is fully covered with azolla in about 8 to 12 days, one side bund is removed, thereby increasing the area to 2000 m^2, with temporary soil bunds as enclosures. The process is repeated on the 14th and 17th day and the area is increased 4000 m^2 and again on the 21st and 24th day to increase the area to 1 ha. The whole 1 ha field is expected to be fully covered before the 30th day.

Inoculation: The amount of inoculum varies according to the time of the year, time available for multiplication of azolla, soil and water fertility conditions. During the long fallow season in cold weather, fields can be inoculated with a low level of azolla ($ > 25$ g/m^2). When azolla needs to be fitted into a short fallow period between crops, much higher levels of inoculum (300 g/m^2) will be required to produce sufficient green manure (Lumpkin and Plucknett 1982). Inoculation rates of 0.4-6.0 kg/m^2 in China, 0.5-0.7 kg/m^2 in Viet Nam, 0.2-0.3 kg/m^2 in the Philippines and 0.1-0.4 kg m^2 in India fresh azolla have been used.

For dual rice/azolla systems in India, inoculation of 0.02 to 0.05 kg/m^2 azolla was used. An even distribution of azolla over the water surface is necessary during inoculation. In the Philippines, about 15 percent of azolla biomass left on the soil surface was allowed to grow with the rice seedlings or azolla was inoculated again at the rate of 200-300 g fresh weight/m^2 at 10-14 days after transplanting of rice (Ventura and Watanabe 1991).

Fertilizer application: As azolla is an aquatic plant, essential elements must be made available in the water for its survival and multiplication. Azolla requires all essential plant nutrients plus Mo and Co for N$_2$ fixation (Yatazawa *et al*. 1980; Becking 1979).

Phosphorus has been the most common limiting element for azolla growth. Successful field cultivation of azolla requires application of P at 0.5-1.0 kg/ha/day. Phosphorus application is usually necessary for the rice crop, but instead of applying it to the rice the P can be given to the azolla in small weekly applications and the phosphorus becomes available to the rice crop on incorporation of azolla. One kg P applied to azolla can result in about 5-10 kg N$_2$-fixation (Lumpkin 1987). Azolla requires a minimum concentration of about 0.2-0.3 percent P on a dry weight basis for a normal N concentration of 3.0-4.0 percent. P deficiency can be overcome by applying P fertilizer in water soluble forms. Phosphorus enriched azolla can multiply 5-7 times after inoculation until it becomes P deficient. The best method of enrichment of azolla with P is to broadcast twice 4.33 kg P/ha at 2-day intervals and to harvest azolla 3 days after P application. Ventura and Watanabe (1991) reported that split application of P fertilizer at 0.9 to 1.3 kg P/ha every week was desirable. It is preferable to soak the fertilizer overnight and then apply in diluted concentration evenly over the azolla mat. According to Pande (1978) the applications of P (1.75 to 3.50 kg P/ha per harvest) and insecticides are necessary for proper growth of azolla.

Application of K has been found to be necessary on light soils in Viet Nam and China (Lu 1966; Vo and Tran 1970). K is used most often during cold weather or in severely deficient soils at rates of 2-5 kg/ha. In very acid soils (pH 4.5 and less), moderate liming may enhance azolla growth. In some deficient soils, the addition of a small amount of Mo and Fe has proved useful in increasing the rate of N fixation of azolla (Rains and Talley 1978).

Incorporation of azolla: Azolla grown as a monocrop or as an intercrop with rice should be incorporated into the soil before its maximum growth density. This will ensure the highest production of green manure and promotes early release of N for the rice. When azolla is grown as monocropped basal green manure for rice, the mat can be incorporated into the soil with regular tillage equipment. The system usually requires draining of the field to ensure contact of the azolla with the soil and to avoid incomplete and uneven incorporation patterns.

Intercropped azolla is usually incorporated by hand into the soil. A small hand-operated or gas-powered rotary type weeder can be used to incorporate the mat of azolla into the soil. The two-way incorporation can be very effective, but the rice must be planted equidistant, both in the rows and between the rows, to allow passing of the weeding machine (Lumpkin and Plucknett 1982).

Genetic Improvement in Azolla

Watanabe and Liu (1990) reported that in order to overcome cultural constraints and to increase N_2-fixing activity, attempts to improve the *Azolla/Anabaena* system by hybridization, and algal inoculation have been successful. Wei *et al*. (1986) reported hybridization between *A. mexicana* and *A. filiculoides*. Hybrids also showed improved tolerance to heat and snail attack. Do Van *et al*. (1989) reported on hybrids between *A. microphylla* and *A. filiculoides*. The N content of field and laboratory-grown hybrids was higher than that of the parent *A. microphylla*. Although these achievements are preliminary, they have opened the way for genetic improvement and for studying the mechanisms of *Azolla/Anabaena* symbiosis.

GREEN-MANURE-BASED CROP ROTATIONS

The most widely-used green-manure crops, such as sesbania, sunn hemp, cowpea, mungbean, clusterbean, etc. are short-day species grown in the summer (mid-year) season in the tropics. In the cooler, sub-tropical climates of China, Japan and the United States, vetches and clovers are the common green-manure crops. These are usually sown in the winter and develop by the following summer when they are incorporated before planting rice and maize. Important green-manure-based crop rotations commonly followed in different countries are indicated in Figure 2.

TRANSPORTED GREEN-MANURING MATERIAL

As an alternative to producing green-manuring material *in situ*, it may be harvested elsewhere and transported to the site of incorporation.

FIGURE 2
Some important green-manure based crop rotations in different countries

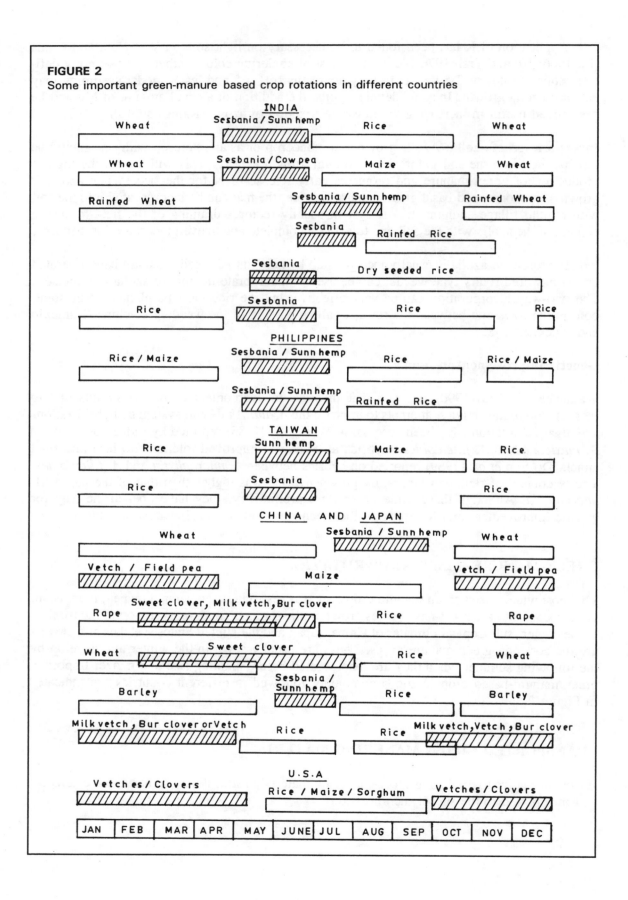

Green-leaf Manuring

In this system, green plant material of readily decomposable nature (low in lignin) is cut from surrounding, mostly wild-growing leguminous herbage and carried to the cropping field for early incorporation. The benefit, as for material produced *in situ*, is mainly due to the N contribution and favourable effects of the organic-matter additions. Since most work has been reported with rice, further discussion is included under that crop in Chapter 7.

The special case of using so called alley-, hedge-, avenue- or row-planting to supply transportable green manure is discussed below.

Alley-cropping

Shifting cultivation, in which one- or two-years' cropping alternates with a bush fallow period of six or more years, is still the dominant food-crop production system throughout 25 percent of the exploitable tropical lands (FAO 1974). Although this system is capable of sustaining agricultural production on uplands in many parts of the tropics, rapid population growth has resulted in widespread shortening of the fallow periods, over-exploitation of the land and consequent soil degradation and low yields (Kang and Wilson 1987). Of the various crop-production systems tested in the humid tropics to replace it, one of the most promising is the alley- or hedge-cropping system (Wilson and Kang 1981; Kang *et al.* 1985; Kang and Wilson 1987). This agroforestry system involves the cultivation in rows of fast-growing perennial legumes bordering a cropping field. These are generally trees that have the ability to fix atmospheric N_2, tap nutrients from deeper layers of the soil and supply N-rich foliage for use as a green manure or mulch for soil-fertility maintenance. This reduces the need for fallow periods, making continuous cultivation possible and enhancing the efficiency of land use.

On alfisols and associated degraded soils *Leucaena leucocephala* and *Gliricidia sepium* are the most promising woody species for alley-cropping (Atta-Krah *et al.* 1985). With proper management, these species can also be successfully grown in semi-arid areas (ICRAF 1987).

Leucaena is planted from seed in rows 4- to 5-m apart at a spacing of 25 cm within rows (Atta-Krah 1990). During the cropping periods, the trees are pruned 4-5 times each year to a height of about 50-75 cm. This minimizes shading of the associated arable crops. In Hawaii, Guevarra *et al.* (1978) reported that good herbage yields from leucaena can be obtained by cutting every three months. Other variables affecting yield include variety, cutting-height and plant density.

The woody leguminous (and non-leguminous) species commonly used as hedgerows in alley-cropping are listed in Annex 1.

Chapter 3

Accumulation of biomass and nitrogen

This section deals with the production from green manures under normal soil conditions; their response under salt-affected soils is reviewed in Chapter 6.

LEGUMINOUS GREEN MANURES

N-accumulation in Herbage

Biomass production and N-accumulation of leguminous green-manure species vary widely under different agroclimatic conditions, age of crop and management practices. Data on biomass from different green-manure species in Asia and Africa are given in Annex 2, in which dry-matter production at 40-49 days and 50-60 days is shown to vary from 1.3 to 4.9 t/ha and from 2.9 to 8.9 t/ha, respectively. Dry matter production by legume green manures in tropical Latin America ranged from 2.5 t/ha with *Zorina lattifolia* to over 13 t/ha with *Crotalaria striata*. The total N accumulation in the above ground matter in a few weeks to a few months varied from 58 to over 300 kg/ha (Annex 2). After harvesting grains, soybean produced 7.5 t/ha of residue which contained 108 kg N/ha (Bowen 1987). In Trinidad, after harvesting grains, cowpeas produced about 1.7 t/ha of residues containing 15 to 20 kg N/ha (Mughogho *et al.* 1982). In Peru, groundnut residues contributed 30 to 50 kg N/ha (Benites *et al.* 1987).

The data on milk vetch in China and Japan show a wide range in fresh-matter production (19-75 t/ha) at flowering. The reason may be that biomass production and N-accumulation of milk vetch increases rapidly after flowering begins (Ishikawa 1963).

Sesbania and sunn hemp are the most productive and widely-used species. Data on biomass from *Sesbania aculeata* at different ages from different locations in India were subjected to regression analysis (Figure 3). The significant linear relationship found between dry-matter production and age of green manure, confirms its wide adaptability to diverse soil and climate conditions.

In the United States, dry-matter yields of different winter legumes ranged from 2.4 to 6.7 t/ha in crimson clover and from 2.7 to 4.2 t/ha in hairy vetch (Table 6). Among summer legumes, pigeonpea, sunn hemp, indigo and joint vetch were the more productive with dry biomass production reaching 13 t/ha for full-season crops (Table 7).

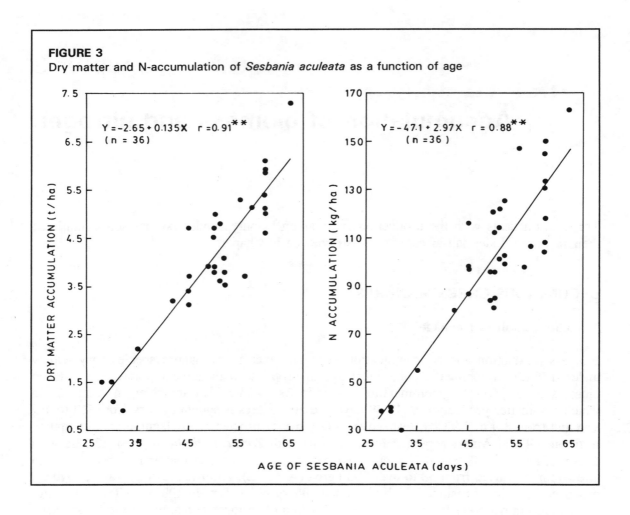

FIGURE 3
Dry matter and N-accumulation of *Sesbania aculeata* as a function of age

TABLE 6
Dry matter and N yields of winter legume crops in the USA

Crop				Reference
Crimson clover	Hairy vetch	Subterranean clover	Winter peas	
Dry matter (t/ha)				
3.2	2.7	-	1.8	Welch *et al.* (1950)
-	2.7	-	1.7	Kamprath *et al.* (1958)
2.4	4.2	-	-	Ebelhar *et al.* (1984)
5.0	-	3.8	-	Dabney *et al.* (1984)
5.3	3.8	6.0	5.6	Hoyt & Hargrove (1986)
6.7	4.2	4.0	-	Hargrove (1986)
N yield (kg/ha)				
147	158	-	-	Mitchell & Teel (1977)
133	133	-	-	Brown *et al.* (1985)
56	209	-	-	Ebelhar *et al.* (1984)
170	153	114	-	Hargrove (1986)
-	-	-	128-203	Mahler & Auld (1989)

Leucaena has been the most widely successful perennial legume used in alley cropping. Fresh herbage yields range from 40 to 80 t/ha/year when moisture is not limiting (Brewbaker 1987). Yields are reduced to 20-50 t/ha in the seasonally-dry tropics. Huxley (1986) summarized the data on biomass production from leucaena hedgerows from different countries. Biomass (dry matter) production in one year was 3.6 t/ha in Indonesia, 20.0 t/ha in India, 5.8-7.0 t/ha in Nigeria and 6.1-17.6 t/ha in various areas of the tropics. In Sri Lanka, gliricidia and leucaena provided about 6 t leaf dry matter/ha per year according to Nair (1988), whereas Weerakoon (1983) reported that leucaena produced 2.8 t leaf dry matter/ha per year; this was equal to approximately 90 kg N, 9 kg P and 73 kg K/ha. Leucaena contains on a dry-weight basis 3.0-3.5 % N, 0.27 % P, 1.40 % K, 0.80 % Ca and 0.14 % S (Brewbaker and Hilton 1979).

Nitrogen accumulation in the tops of several commonly-used leguminous green manures is also given in Annex 2. Values in India ranged from 25 to 163 kg N/ha and in the Philippines up to 226 kg N/ha. In China, milk vetch and sesbania accumulated 101-375 kg N/ha at full flowering, while in Senegal *Aeschynomene* exceeded 500 kg N/ha in microplot experiments. Yields of over 100 kg N/ha are common in 50- to 60-day-old sesbania and sunn hemp. In the Philippines, Hernandez et al. (1957) found that N yield, as with dry-matter production, was linearly related to the age of the crop. Morris *et al.* (1986a), however, observed that although different green manures showed a linear relationship between N accumulation and dry weight irrespective of species, they were affected by age of the crop. A maximum N content of 2.45 percent was observed at 45 days and values fell to 1.88 percent at 60 days. Evans *et al.* (1989) also observed that N accumulation in field peas and narrow-leaf lupins was linearly related to dry-matter production ($r^2 = 0.93$). Ishikawa (1963) reported that the N yield of milk vetch was 108 kg/ha at the initiation of flowering and increased to 156 kg N/ha during flowering (14 days later).

In the USA, Table 6 shows that winter legume crops accumulated 56-209 kg N/ha but in most cases it was between 100 and 150 kg N/ha. In Louisiana, subterranean clover was found to contain 104 kg N/ha in mid-March and 165 kg N/ha in mid-April (Eastman 1986). Mahler and Auld (1989) reported 128 to 203 kg N/ha accumulated by Austrian winter peas. Summer legumes accumulated 170 to 250 kg N/ha in the full season (Table 7). In Hawaii, Evans and Rotar (1987b) reported that high-yielding accessions of annual sesbania produced 8-17 t/ha dry matter containing 150-245 kg N/ha when sown at 125 000 plants/ha and harvested at the late stage of 90 days after sowing.

In long-term studies in Nigeria, Kang *et al.* (1985) and Atta-Krah (1990) reported that the N yield from leucaena prunings ranged from 156 to 208 kg/ha/year. On degraded land, leucaena and gliricidia prunings gave higher nutrient yields than those of some widely-used non-leguminous native species such as *Acioa barterii* or *Alchornea cordifolia* (Table 7). Hauser (1990) reported that leucaena in hedgerow plantings added 59 kg N/ha per pruning on an average of five prunings per year. Mulongoy and Sanginga (1990) reported that leucaena in alley-cropping fixed 134 to 174 kg N/ha/year.

Mercado *et al.* (1989) evaluated the performance of tree legume hedgerows in farmers' fields on a sloping acid upland environment in the Philippines. They identified four tree legumes species adapted to contour bunds: *Gliricidia sepium, Cassia spectabilis, Flemingia congesta* and *Casia siamea*. The mean biomass production and nutrient yield of *Gliricidia sepium* of 6 m wide alleys between two hedgerows across five locations during the year 1988-

TABLE 7
Dry matter and N yields of tropical legumes grown during various seasons in the USA
(Reddy *et al*. 1986)

Green-manure crop	Dry matter (t/ha)			N yield (kg/ha)		
	Early[a]	Full[b]	Late[c]	Early	Full	Late
Mungbean	2.1	-	2.8	30	-	40
Pigeonpea	9.5	13.3	8.8	190	250	180
Crotalaria spectabilis	9.1	10.2	5.7	160	170	90
Indigo	9.0	13.0	6.2	170	220	110
Joint vetch	7.8	10.0	6.9	170	170	150

[a]   15 April to 15 August
[b]   15 April to 15 September
[c]   7 June to 15 September

TABLE 8
Biological nitrogen fixation by legume green manure crops

Species	Growing season	Age (days)	% Ndfa	Method	Reference
S. rostrata	Long day	56	88	ARA/^{15}N$_2$	Becker *et al.* (1990)
	Short day	56	83		
A. afrespera	Long day	56	77		
	Short day	56	68		
S. rostrata	Long day	45	88	N^{15} dilution	Pareek *et al.* (1990)
		55	91		
	Short day	45	71		
		55	83		
S. cannabina	Long day	45	93		
		55	94		
	Short day	45	77		
		55	83		
S. aculeata	Long day	52	80	Difference method	Meelu *et al.* (1990)
S. cannabina	Long day	Flowering	72-95	^{15}N dilution	Chapman & Myers (1987)
Clovers and vetches	Short day	Flowering	67-84		Smith *et al.* (1987)

89 was 1.76 t DM/ha, 53 kg/ha N, 3.9 kg P, 8.0 kg K, 9.7 kg Mg and 23.6 kg Ca/ha. In Hawaii, Rosecrance and Kuo (1989) tested nine leguminous tree species in alley farming and obtained green leaf manure yield ranging from 0.6 t/ha (*L. salvadorensis*) to 6.4 t/ha (*S. sesban*).

The foregoing review of experimental data exemplifies the wide range of values for N-accumulation to be expected taking into account differences in growing environment, age of crop and species used. It is concluded that the most productive green-manure crops in terms of biomass and N-accumulation are *Sesbania* spp., which are widely used in lowland-rice systems in Asia.

N-accumulation in Roots

The contribution of roots to total N-accumulation is generally small in most leguminous green manures. In sesbania, crimson clover and hairy vetch, N-accumulation in roots ranged from 9 to 28 kg/ha, or 9 to 13 percent of the total N accumulated in roots plus shoots (Mitchell and Teel 1977; Palm *et al*. 1988; Beri *et al*. 1989b; Meelu *et al*, 1990).

Soil-N versus Fixed-N

A few measurements have been made on the proportion of plant N derived from atmospheric fixation. Different methods of its measurement have been discussed by Peoples *et al*. (1988). The simple difference method assumes that leguminous and non-leguminous crops take up the same quantity of soil N, and that an insignificant amount of the non-legume N is derived from atmospheric fixation. Better methods include the use of a non-nodulating cultivar of the same legume as a control, and the ^{15}N isotope-dilution technique. Using the latter technique, Chapman and Myers (1987) estimated that 60-72 percent of the total N accumulated by sesbania and soybean was from atmospheric fixation when they were grown after 12 months of fallow, and 93-95 percent when they immediately followed a dry-season crop. Table 8 shows percent N fixed from atmosphere by different legumes using different techniques. Evans *et al*. (1989) reported that N_2 fixation by lupin and peas averaged 61 and 65 percent, respectively (but it was highly variable, ranging from 20 to 97 percent).

The wide variation in the quoted data may reflect variation in efficiency of nodulation but values of 70-90 percent appear generally attainable.

AZOLLA

Azolla pinnata contains 4-5 percent N on a dry-weight basis, and 0.2 to 0.3 percent on a fresh-weight basis containing about 94 percent moisture (Pande 1978). Azolla has a high growth rate and can accumulate more than 10 kg N/ha/day (Lumpkin 1987). Roger and Watanabe (1986) reported that azolla fixed from 0.4 to 3.6 kg N/ha/day (average 2 kg N/ha/day). Pande (1978) found that azolla increased its green mass two- to five-fold in a week. Experiments conducted in different countries showed considerable N contribution from azolla (Table 9). The amount of N harvested from azolla in one year reached 840 kg/ha (excluding N added from inoculum) in India (Singh 1979; Singh 1982), and 1075 kg/ha in China (Li *et al*. 1982), (about one-third of the N being supplied as inoculum). Watanabe *et al*. (1977) working with *A. pinnata* observed an eight-fold increase in azolla-N over the amount inoculated in 106 days; Singh (1979) found an 18- to 28-fold increase (between 24 and 37 kg N/ha in 35 days); and Rains and Talley (1979) reported a nearly 30-fold increase with *A. mexicana* (41 kg N/ha in 46 days). As also shown in Table 9 application of P fertilizer considerably increased growth and N accumulation of azolla (Satapathy and Singh 1985).

TABLE 9
Biomass and N-accumulation by azolla in flooded rice fields

Type of study	Biomass (t/ha)	N fixed (kg/ha)	Period	Reference
Field, monthly inoculation and weekly azolla harvest	333	840	year	Singh (1979)
Concrete tanks	321	800	year	Singh (1982)
Continuous cultivation				
A. pinnata (India) No P 3.5 kg P/ha/week	172 343	234 755	year	Satapathy & Singh (1985)
A. pinnata (Viet Nam/Thailand) No P 3.5 kg P/ha/week	224-234 382-390	334-364 885-913		
Field study, intercrop	-	300	year	Liu (1979)
Cropped green manure	-	540-675	year	
Laboratory study	-	103-162	year	Becking (1979)
Field, intercrop	-	117	106 days	Watanabe *et al.* (1977)
Field inoculation	-	51-92	46 days	Rains & Talley (1979)
Field, continuous cultivation, 4 different species of azolla	-	1075	year	Li *et al.* (1982)
Field study (mean of wet and dry seasons) two intercrops two intercrops plus basal	29 46	53 73	40 days 60 days	Singh & Singh (1989)
Field study	55	139	year	Beri & Meelu (1983)

There have been few measurements of the proportion of N that azolla derives from atmospheric fixation under field conditions. Lowendorf (1982) suggested that only half of azolla-N grown in the field resulted from N_2-fixation, but Watanabe and Liu (1990) reported that 80-85 percent of azolla-N is so derived. The amount of N accumulated by one crop of azolla ranged from 20 to 121 kg/ha (Rains and Talley 1979; Watanabe and Liu 1990) and by azolla intercropped with rice from 8 to 75 kg/ha.

Regarding species differences, Li (1984) reported that *A. microphylla* fixed about three times more N in summer than did *A. filiculoides*. Conversely, in winter *A. filiculoides* fixed eight times more than *A. microphylla*.

These findings demonstrate the high potential for rapid accumulation of atmospheric N_2 by azolla, and point to the importance of selecting species on the basis of their seasonal adaptability. Utilization of azolla-N by rice is discussed in Chapter 7.

Chapter 4

Nutrient transformation in the soil

The rate and extent of mineralization of incorporated green manure, and release of constituent minerals, depends largely on soil conditions such as pH, temperature, moisture content, aeration status, biotic activity, etc. The fates of individual nutrients are reviewed below.

NITROGEN

The net release of N from incorporated manure is dictated by the balance of the N-transformation processes of mineralization and immobilization. Factors determining decomposition and mineralization kinetics of N include N content, C/N ratio and lignin content, which are primarily governed by species and age of the green-manure crop.

Frankenberger and Abdelmagid (1985) considered that the critical C/N ratio for N mineralization from legume residues was <19:1. Vlek *et al.* (1981) reported that faster mineralization occurs at C/N ratios below 25:1. John *et al.* (1989c) reported that initially, N-mineralization from cowpea green manure (C/N ratio 15:1) was faster than from cowpea residue (C/N ratio 21:1), but at 30 days after transplanting, mineral-N was higher in residue-incorporated plots.

In a study on four Philippine rice soils, however, Nagarajah *et al.* (1989) found that ammonium-N release from *Azolla microphylla* was slower and lower than that from *S. rostrata*, despite its lower C/N ratio. The difference was attributed to the higher lignin content of *A. microphylla* (20 percent versus 9 percent). Shi *et al.* (1981) reported that recovery of N by a first rice crop was 25.4 and 37.6 percent from azolla and milk vetch, respectively. Both materials had almost similar C/N ratios (11.2 and 11.8), but azolla had the greater amount of lignin (20.2 vs. 13.5 percent).

Kundu *et al.* (1990) found that rate and magnitude of N-release from gliricidia were higher than from sesbania when incorporated into submerged rice fields at transplanting. The gliricidia material consisted of green twigs and leaves that had a lower lignin content than the sesbania material, which consisted of whole plants. In pot culture using alluvial sandy loam soil (pH 7.4), Bhardwaj and Dev (1985) found that release of mineral N after 49 days of incubation under flooded conditions was 112, 80 and 76 kg/ha with 45-, 55- and 65-day old sesbania, respectively. This confirms the depressing effect on N-release of increasing levels of lignin with crop development towards flowering.

Ishikawa (1963) reported that decomposition and N-release from milk vetch green manure increased with increasing temperatures from 18°C to 30°C. At 30°C, N-mineralization was maximum (70 percent of the original N) following 30 days of incubation. Groffman *et al.* (1987) and Varro *et al.* (1987) reported that clover residue incorporated into soil decayed nearly twice as fast as that left on the surface. Several authors confirm that N-mineralization proceeds more rapidly under anaerobic than under aerobic conditions (Tusneem and Patrick 1971; Watanabe 1984; Gale and Gilmour 1988).

In laboratory and field studies, Singh *et al.* (1981b), Khind *et al.* (1985), Yadvinder-Singh *et al.* (1988b) and Bhardwaj and Dev (1985) showed that release of mineral N from green manure was initially rapid, but slowed markedly within a fairly short time. Frankenberger and Abdelmagid (1985) found that N-mineralization from legume residues under field capacity water regime followed first-order kinetics with

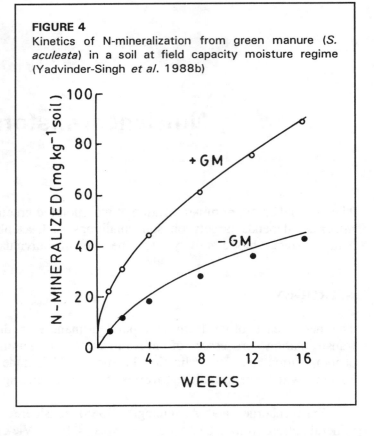

FIGURE 4

Kinetics of N-mineralization from green manure (*S. aculeata*) in a soil at field capacity moisture regime (Yadvinder-Singh *et al.* 1988b)

N-mineralization-rate constants ranging from 0.045 to 0.325/week. Yadvinder-Singh *et al.* (1988b) showed that the N-mineralization kinetics of green manure under aerobic conditions could be modelled by two simultaneous first-order reactions (Figure 4) — an initial fast reaction (k=2.12/week), followed by a slow release of inorganic N (k=0.069/week).

Under waterlogged conditions in the absence of rice plants, N-release increased rapidly up to 2 weeks and reached a plateau (Aspiras 1966; Nagarajah 1988; Nagarajah *et al.* 1989). In the presence of rice plants, soil-solution ammonium-N peaked 2 to 4 weeks after addition of *Sesbania aculeata* and then declined to a low level 6 to 8 weeks later (Figure 5). The decline was attributed largely to rice-plant uptake, and also to losses of N via nitrification-denitrification and volatilization as NH_3. The time of peak mineral-N release from the green manure varied greatly, however, in different studies (Singh *et al.* 1981b; Bhardwaj and Dev 1985; Khind *et al.* 1987b; Beri *et al.* 1989b).

Incorporation of green manure affects NH_3-volatilization through its influence on soil pH and P_{CO_2}. In soils ranging in texture from sandy loam to clay loam, and in pH from 7.4 to 10.0, various workers have shown that green manuring reduces NH_3-volatilization losses by decreasing pH (Venkatakrishnan 1980; Rao and Batra 1983; Santra *et al.* 1988; Sarvanan *et al.* 1988; Khind *et al.* 1989). However, John *et al.* (1989a) observed that incorporating cowpea green manure 15 days before transplanting rice had no effect on urea-N loss via denitrification. Low levels of nitrate in the flood water following urea application suggested that N loss from denitrification of urea was controlled by supply of nitrate rather than availability of organic C from the green manure. Bhagat *et al.* (1988) reported that leaching losses of N from urea (90 kg N/ha) or from green manure + urea (1:1 N equivalent) were small but similar. John *et al.* (1989b) observed that green manuring had no effect on N loss from urea

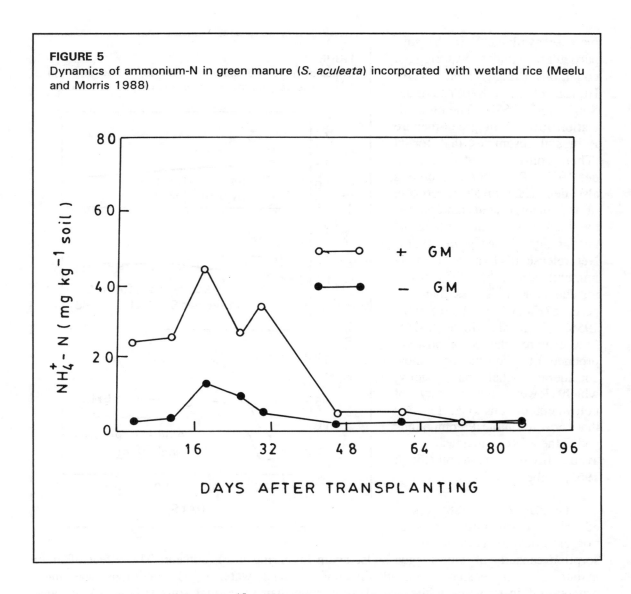

FIGURE 5
Dynamics of ammonium-N in green manure (*S. aculeata*) incorporated with wetland rice (Meelu and Morris 1988)

applied to rice as assessed from ^{15}N balances and pNH_3 in the flood water. In an acid clay-loam soil, average loss of ammoniacal N from ammonium sulphate and sunn hemp applied separately and jointly, was 23.2, 20.4 and 16.2 percent, respectively (Huang *et al*. 1981).

Interpretation of the results of such studies as reported above must take into account the time-scale equilibrium between mineralization from the green manure (and the soil itself), loss as NH_3 and uptake by the succeeding crop, particularly where wetland rice is concerned.

The economically important issue of N-recovery from green manures and its fertilizer equivalence is reviewed later in relation to the response of rice — the area that has received the most attention.

PHOSPHORUS

Leguminous green manure crops recycle P from the sub-soil (Subbiah and Mannikar 1964), release P on mineralization in the soil (Bin 1983; Singh 1984; Blair and Boland 1978) and increase available P in the soil, particularly under waterlogged conditions (Singh *et al*. 1981b; Hundal *et al*. 1987; Yadvinder Singh *et al*. 1988b). The mineralization process of green-manure P in soil resembles that for N (Thompson *et al*. 1954; Alexander 1977). Phosphorus release is also dependant on the P content of the incorporated material — the higher it is, the greater its availability (Fuller *et al*. 1956). Net release of P is reduced by immobilization if the plant-residue content is less than 0.3 percent (Kaila 1954; Fuller *et al*. 1956; Singh and Jones 1976). Furthermore, the decomposition products of green manures show considerable chelation capacity, which lowers the activity of polyvalent cations (Ca, Fe, Al) that form insoluble P compounds and therefore increases the availability of P in the soil (Singh 1962; Agboola 1974).

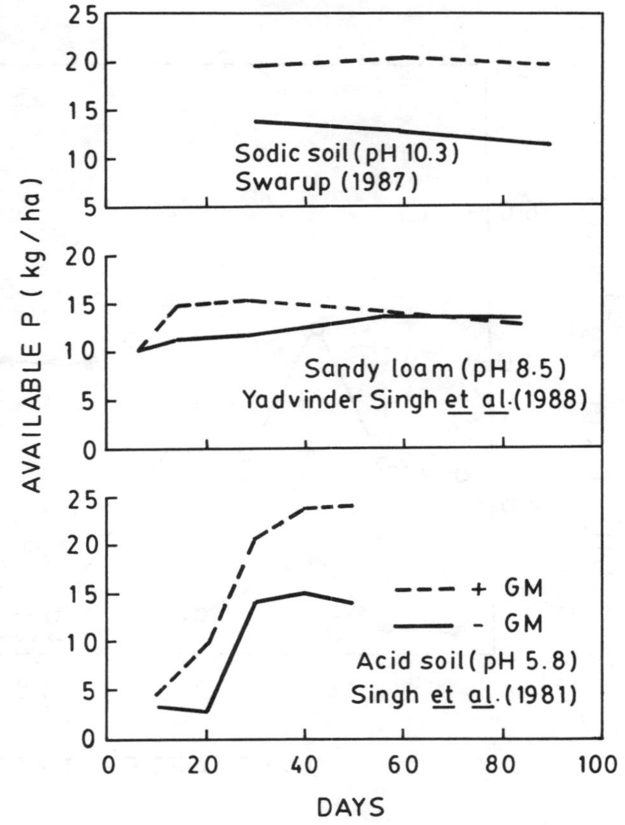

Hundal *et al*. (1988) reported that green-manure incorporation significantly reduced the P-

FIGURE 6

Effect of green manuring on changes in available P in three soils varying in pH under submerged conditions

sorption capacity of waterlogged soils, again favouring net P content. The effect of green manuring in increasing the availability of P under waterlogged conditions was more pronounced in strongly acidic and alkaline soils than in normal soils (Figure 6), because green-manure materials tend to modify soil pH towards neutrality. Singh *et al*. (1981b) also reported that pH changes in a submerged acid soil amended with organic residues were significantly correlated with available P.

Effects of green manure on P transformation in soils are expected to be smaller under upland (aerobic) than under waterlogged (anaerobic) conditions, owing to the lower metabolic efficiencies of anaerobic microbial populations.

However in a laboratory study carried out by Yadvinder-Singh *et al*. (1988b) under upland conditions, green manuring with sesbania did not appreciably increase the available-P content of a sandy-loam soil. Singh and Rai (1973) and Bajpai *et al*. (1980) reported slightly greater build-up of inorganic P due to green manuring under upland situations in normal, than in saline and alkaline soils.

Blair and Boland (1978) observed that P derived from whole white-clover plants by 36-day-old oat plants was 2.8 and 5.2 percent on low P and high P soils, respectively. Hundal *et al*. (1987) observed utilization by 8-week-old rice of P from cowpea, clusterbean and sesbania to range from 11.2 to 13.2 percent.

TABLE 10
Characteristics of roots of some green manure crops and utilization of difficultly-available nutrients (Gu and Wen 1981)

Crop	CEC meq/100 g dry root	Respiratory intensity mg CO_2/g dry root/h	Increment of dry matter (%)		
			Apatite	Orthoclase	Serpentine
Milk vetch	47.0	5.01	312	40	30
Vetch	41.9	3.91	183	15	53
Wheat	20.5	1.86	102	12	21

TABLE 11
Effect of alley cropping *Leucaena leucocephala* with maize and cowpea on some chemical properties of surface soil (0-15 cm) after six years (Kang *et al.* 1985)

Treatment (*Leucaena* prunings)	pH	Organic C (%)	Exchangeable nutrients (meq/100 g)			Available P (kg/ha)
			K	Ca	Mg	
Control	6.0	0.65	0.19	2.90	0.35	54
Incorporated	6.0	1.07	0.28	3.45	0.50	52
Incorporated + 80 kg N/ha	5.8	1.19	0.26	2.80	0.45	51
LSD (p=0.05)	0.2	0.14	0.05	0.55	0.11	NS

These results indicate that modest amounts of green-manure-P become available to a following crop on incorporation, but there is some difficulty in distinguishing between the added P and that mobilized from the soil by decomposition of the green manure.

POTASSIUM, CALCIUM, MAGNESIUM AND SULPHUR

Many workers have reported increased availability of K in soils as a result of green manuring (Kute and Mann 1969; Debnath and Hajra 1972; Katyal 1977; Nagarajah *et al.* 1989; Tiwari *et al.* 1980; Swarup 1987). According to Agboola (1974) carbon dioxide and organic acids released during decomposition of green manures may act on insoluble soil minerals thereby releasing nutrients into the soil solution. Leguminous green manure plants, because of their higher root-respiratory characteristics, possess a strong ability to absorb difficultly available K and P from the soil (Table 10). Ploughing-in of crimson clover resulted in an increase in the levels of P, K, Ca and Mg in the soil (Groffman *et al.* 1987). Kang *et al* (1985) and Atta-Krah (1990) in long-term studies of incorporating leucaena prunings on soil chemical properties showed that they significantly increased organic matter and exchangeable K, Ca and Mg levels (Table 11).

Katyal (1977) and Khind *et al.* (1987a) also observed significant increases in water-soluble Ca and Mg with application of green manures to flooded soils. The peaks of Ca and Mg concentration were observed 8 days after application of the green manure.

It is generally believed that organic manures with S content of more than 0.15 percent will undergo S release during decomposition (Biederbeck 1978). Dhillon and Dhillon (1991) used ^{35}S-labelled green manure and observed that cowpea and clusterbean plants containing 0.33 and 0.27 percent total S, supplied 18.4 and 20.0 percent S, respectively to toria (*Brassica campestris* var. toria).

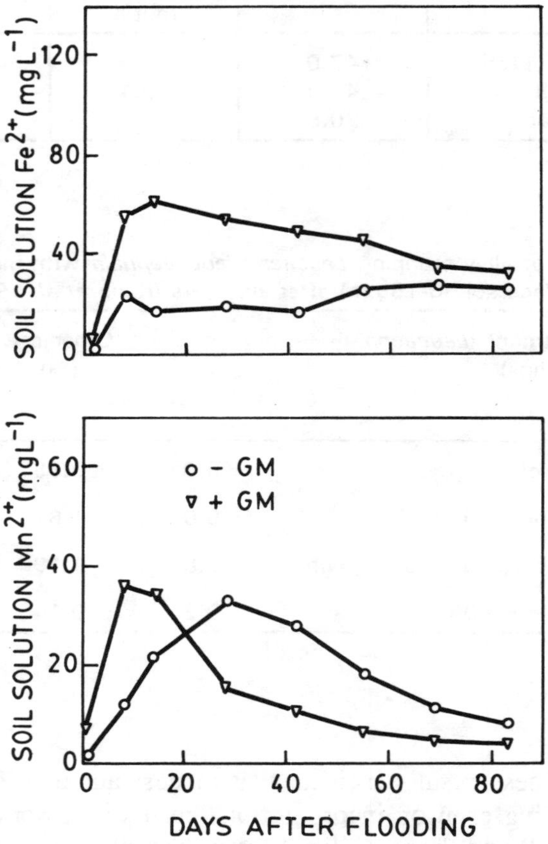

MICRONUTRIENTS

As well as being a source of micronutrient *per se*, green manuring influences micronutrient transformations through changes in oxidation-reduction regimes and increased chelation capacity. In a number of studies, increase in soil solution Fe^{2+} and Mn^{2+} with submergence was accelerated when calcareous and non-calcareous soils (Thind and Chahal 1983), black, red and lateritic soils (Katyal 1977), sodic soils (Sadana and Bajwa 1985), neutral (Khind *et al*. 1987a) and acidic soils (Nagarajah *et al*.

FIGURE 7

Effect of sesbania green manuring on changes in concentration of soil solution Fe^{2+} and Mn^{2+} in a flooded soil

1989) were green-manured. In all these soils, peak Fe^{2+} concentration was recorded about 2 weeks after submergence. For Mn^{2+}, the peak generally appeared at 1 or 2 weeks after submergence. In saline-sodic soils, with very low levels of soil-solution Mn^{2+}, Sadana and Bajwa (1985) observed peaks between 4 to 6 weeks after submergence. A typical example of the transformation dynamics of Fe^{2+} and Mn^{2+} in a green-manured soil is shown in Figure 7 (Nagarajah *et al*. 1989).

Water-soluble Fe^{2+} and Mn^{2+} occur in the soil solution in two forms — ionic and chelated. Studies by Bao *et al*. (1978, 1983) and Bao and Yu (1986) showed that concentrations of chelated Fe^{2+} peaked at 4 to 7 days after green manure began to decompose, and decreased after 10 days; the peak period for chelated Mn^{2+} was even earlier. Yu (1985) suggested that rice plants can grow normally on some strongly-reducing soils where the concentration of water-soluble Fe^{2+} is high because a considerable amount of the ion is in the chelated form.

In a laboratory study, Bijay-Singh *et al*. (1992) observed greater increase in DTPA-extractable Fe and Mn with sesbania (2g/kg soil) in a submerged soil than in one at field-capacity moisture. Sharma and Katyal (1982) in field microplots also obtained an increase in

DTPA-extractable Fe with sesbania green manuring. A marked increase in DTPA-extractable Fe and Mn has also been reported following manuring of wetland rice with mungbean (*Vigna radiata*) haulm (Meelu and Rekhi 1981). Swarup (1987) observed an increase in ammonium-acetate-extractable Fe and Mn following green manuring with sesbania. Chahal and Khera (1988) found that green manure increased the $0.5\underline{N}$-$CaCl_2$-extractable Fe under 50 percent soil-saturation. Gopala Rao (1956) reported increased Fe- and Mn-availability (extractable with Morgan's reagent) and shoot weight of rice, green-manured with gliricidia in a red soil.

In a field experiment on a coarse-textured soil, Nayyar and Takkar (1989) found that Fe deficiency in wetland rice was more effectively corrected by sesbania green manure than by soil-applied ferrous sulphate (Figure 8). Similarly, Maskina *et al.* (1985) observed increased availability of Fe in the soil and amelioration of Fe deficiency in a rice nursery amended with green manure. Sharma and Katyal (1982) demonstrated that green manuring with sesbania produced higher dry-matter yield and Fe^{2+} content of 30-day-old seedlings than those receiving soil application of ferrous sulphate or the control (Table 12).

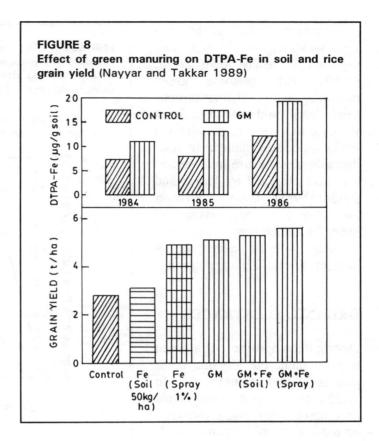

FIGURE 8

Effect of green manuring on DTPA-Fe in soil and rice grain yield (Nayyar and Takkar 1989)

TABLE 12

Effect of green manure and soil application of iron sulphate on dry matter yield, incidence of chlorosis and Fe^{2+} content of rice seedlings (Sharma and Katyal 1982)

Treatment	Dry matter (g/25 plants)	Symptoms (scale 0-5)	Fe^{2+} content (ppm)
Iron sulphate	4.1	4	60
Green manure	7.2	0	80
Control	3.9	4	52
CD (p = 0.05)	1.22	-	-

Several workers (Katyal 1977; Iu *et al.* 1981; Bijay-Singh *et al.* 1992; Khind *et al.* 1987a; Thind and Chahal 1987) observed a decline in water-soluble or DTPA-extractable Zn with flooding, which was accentuated by green manuring in most of the investigations. However, in a sodic soil of pH 10.2, green manure increased the availability of applied Zn (Swarup 1987) because of its effect on lowering the pH. However Bijay-Singh *et al.* (1992) did not find that sesbania green manuring reduced DTPA-extractable Zn at field-capacity moisture levels.

Increase in the availability of DTPA-extractable Cu has been reported by Bijay-Singh *et al.* (1992) with sesbania green manuring in a flooded calcareous sandy-loam soil. A significant increase in DTPA-extractable Cu by incorporating mungbean residue as green manure into the soil was also recorded by Meelu and Rekhi (1981). Green manuring has, therefore, been shown to exert a liberating effect on inherent soil contents of a number of micro plant nutrients.

ORGANIC SUBSTANCES

During decomposition of a green manure numerous organic compounds accumulate in the soil. In aerobic soils, organic compounds decompose liberating CO_2; little accumulation of organic acids occurs under normal soil temp-

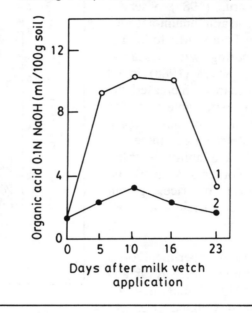

FIGURE 9

Changes in organic-acid concentrations in the soil with time of flooding after incorporation of milk vetch green manure (Ishikawa 1963)

1 = simultaneous flooding and milk vetch incorporation
2 = flooding 5 days after milk vetch incorporation

erature and moisture conditions. Under anaerobic conditions, however, Ishikawa (1988) showed that significant amounts of organic acids accumulate when milk vetch is incorporated with simultaneous flooding. Less build up of organic acids occurs if flooding is delayed by 5 days (Figure 9), because there is rapid production and decomposition of organic acids during the aerobic phase.

Wang *et al.* (1967) reported the accumulation of volatile fatty acids (mainly acetic, and more so in waterlogged than in aerobic conditions), nonvolatile aliphatic acids (mainly malic acid in aerobic, and tartaric and malonic acids in waterlogged soils) and phenolic acids (p-hydroxybenzoic, vanillic and p-coumaric acids) in soils amended with sunn hemp. Watanabe (1984) reported that both acetic and butyric acids accumulated in large quantities when green manure was incorporated under waterlogged conditions. Fujii *et al.* (1972) detected accumulation of amines during decomposition of clover residues.

Organic acids retard root elongation, restrict nutrient uptake and reduce shoot weight (Watanabe 1984). Acetic-acid concentrations exceeding 1 mmol/l restrict P and K uptake (Rao and Mikkelson 1977). Because of the O_2-release and oxidizing ability of rice roots, some metabolites may be absorbed directly or oxidized, either by the rice roots or indirectly by the rhizosphere microorganisms (Watanabe 1984). Green manuring can stimulate formation of ethylene in the soil, which has plant-hormone properties and may also be a regulating agent for plant pathogeneity and root growth (Smith 1976; Primrose 1979). To understand the possible toxicity or stimulation that green manuring causes in the rice plant, the quantitative determination of the metabolites *in situ* is necessary, particulary in the presence of rice plants.

Chapter 5

Effect on soil properties

BIOLOGICAL PROPERTIES

Microfauna

Considerable information exists on the microbiology of soils amended with crop residues and animal manures, but studies on the effects of green manuring on microbial activity are limited.

Kute and Mann (1968), Ramaswami and Raj (1973), and Thomas and Shantaram (1984) recorded a considerable increase in the population of *Azotobacter* and other bacteria, and microbial biomass in soils amended with green manure (Tables 13 and 14). These results together with data from Gupta *et al.* (1983) show that N_2-fixing populations are stimulated by green manuring. The addition of organic matter from alley-cropping increased microbial activity as measured by increased biomass carbon, and reduced soil bulk-density (Yamoah *et al.* 1986a, b). Gopalaswamy and Vidhyasekaran (1987) found nearly a six-fold increase in microbial activity in soil amended with gliricidia (Table 13).

Soil-enzymatic activity is a better indicator of soil microbial activity than plate counts. Bolton *et al.* (1985) compared (a) soils that had grown leguminous crops since 1909, and more recently Austrian winter peas (*Pisum sativum*) as green manure, with (b) soils that had received regular applications of anhydrous ammonia, P and S for the last 30 years. It was found that urease, phosphatase and dehydrogenase activities were significantly higher in (a) (Table 15). Similar results were obtained by Thomas and Shantaram (1984) in a coconut rhizosphere supplied with green manure (Table 14). Bolton *et al.* (1985) also observed a marked decrease in the *Nitrosomonas* population in soil amended with green manure, while the population of denitrifying organisms was slightly increased (Table 15).

Germani *et al.* (1983) reported a marked decrease in the nematode population in rice soil in the presence of green manure, and Reddy *et al.* (1986) found that the use of selected leguminous green manures in a multiple-cropping system reduced soil populations of root-knot nematodes.

Green manures, by providing energy and nutrients, encourage the growth and activity of desirable micro-organisms that play a key role in transforming and liberating plant nutrients in the soil, and also discourage some undesirable ones.

TABLE 13
Effect of green manuring on bacterial population and microbial activity of soil

Treatment	Bacterial population (Kute & Mann 1968)		Microbial activity[a] (in units[b]) (Gopalaswamy & Vidhyasekaran 1987)
	Total bacteria (x 10^3)	Azotobacter (x 10^3)	
-GM	29.4	97.1	17.5 ± 5.0
+GM	44.1	148.9	100 ± 24.5
% increase	49	53	471

[a] measured as dehydrogenase activity
[b] 1 unit = optimal density of 0.001 at 546 nm

TABLE 14
Effect of green manure (*Pueraria phaseoloides*) on microbial population (per g oven-dry soil) and enzyme activity of coconut rhizosphere (Thomas and Shantaram 1984)

A. Microbial population						
Treatment	Bacteria (x 10^6)	Fungi (x 10^6)	Actino-mycetes (x 10^4)	Symbiotic N_2 fixers (x 10^3)	P solubilizers	
					Fungi (x 10^3)	Bacteria (x 10^4)
-GM	18.6	2.3	6.9	41.4	1.2	1.8
+GM	39.3	8.8	18.8	69.3	7.9	7.5
LSD (p=0.05)	10.08	2.75	2.98	NS	2.73	NS

B. Enzyme activity				
	Dehydrogenase activity (μg TPF/g)[a]		Phosphatase activity (μg PNP/g)[b]	Urease activity (μg NH_4^+ -N/g)
	Endo-genous	Response to glucose		
-GM	1.6	5.5	50.9	68.3
+GM	4.1	22.2	62.2	93.1
LSD (p=0.05)	1.41	8.40	NS	11.41

[a] TPF = triphenyl formazan
[b] PNP = p-nitrophenol

TABLE 15
Effect of green manure on microbial population, enzymes and microbial biomass (Bolton *et al*. 1985)

Treatment	Microbial population		Enzymes			Microbial biomass (mg/100 g soil)
	Nitro-somonas (x 10^4)	Denitri-fiers (x 10^5)	Urease[a]	Phospha-tase[b]	Dehydro-genase[c]	
-GM	15.5	2.3	1.7	3.0	5.9	248
+GM	2.3	3.4	2.5	3.5	8.6	314

[a] = 10^{-2} μmol NH_4^+-N/g/min
[b] = 10^{-2} μmol p-nitrophenol/g/min
[c] = 10^{-5} μmol triphenyl formazan/g/min

TABLE 16
Effect of green manuring on soil organic C and N contents under different climates

Green manure	No. of years	Organic (%)		Total N (%)		Reference
		-GM	+GM	-GM	+GM	
A. Soils under rice - tropical and sub-tropical						
Various legumes	-	1.17	1.51	0.079	1.15	Sanyasi Raju (1952)
Milk vetch	14	0.73	0.89	0.092	0.120	Yamazaki (1957)
Sunn hemp	13	0.44	0.48	-	-	Biswas *et al.* (1970)
S. aculeata	10	0.62	0.67	0.045	0.059	Sahu & Nayak (1971)
S. bispinosa + Ipomoea carnea	2 (4 crops)	0.89	0.97	-	-	Chatterjee *et al.* (1979)
S. cannabina	2	0.24	0.30	-	-	Bhardwaj *et al.* (1981)
Milk vetch	3	0.72	0.84	0.146	0.153	Jiao *et al* (1986)
Milk vetch	13	1.53	1.87	0.162	0.184	Ishikawa (1988)
Milk vetch	54	2.76	2.89	0.255	0.298	
S. aculeata/Sunn hemp	2	0.41	0.45	-	-	Sharma & Mittra (1988)
S. aculeata	2	0.23	0.31	-	-	Swarup (1988)
S. aculeata/Sunn hemp		1.15	1.34	0.116	0.131	Meelu *et al.* (1992)
B. Soils under other crops - cool and humid						
Vetch	40	2.9	3.4	0.148	0.171	Prince *et al.* (1941)
Legumes & non-legumes	25	3.17	3.55	-	-	Poyser *et al.* (1957)
Various legumes	18	1.74	1.90	-	-	Mann (1959)
Sunn hemp	32	0.24	0.23	-	-	Singh (1967)
	50	0.37	0.36	-	-	
Various legumes	20	2.44	2.80	-	-	Sowden & Atkinson (1968)
	20	1.23	1.51	-	-	
Sunn hemp	6	0.24	0.26	-	-	Singh & Verma (1969)
Trefoil	30	0.75	0.89	-	-	Chater & Gasser (1970)
Sunn hemp	22	0.40	0.42	0.045	0.046	Maurya & Ghosh (1972)
Crimson clover/Hairy vetch	2	0.79	0.91	0.055	0.073	Hargrove (1986)

Organic Carbon

Green manures add both organic matter and N to the soil. Build-up of organic matter is, however, controlled by the quantity and chemical nature of the green biomass, soil type, climatic factors and cultural practices (MacRae and Mehyus 1985). Meelu *et al.* (1992) found that organic carbon in soil was determined by quantity of green manure added. Shi *et al.* (1981) reported that the higher the lignin content of added green manure, the higher was the humification coefficient — the fraction of organic carbon left after one year of decomposition. Gu and Wen (1981) reported that the humification coefficient of green manures ranged from 0.18 for milk vetch to 0.43 for lignin-rich azolla. Wen (1984) gives as typical humification coefficients 0.10, 0.20 and 0.40 for leaves, aerial parts and roots of milk-vetch green manure, respectively. Warman (1980) stated that plant material low in N (1.5 percent or less on a dry-weight basis) improved the organic-matter content of a soil. However, De Haan (1977), working with a sandy and a clayey soil in The Netherlands, found no correlation between N content of the added material and the amount of organic matter accumulated over 10 years, but he did find a highly significant correlation with the lignin content of the added plant material. Tillage practices also significantly influence organic matter and N accumulation in soils. Utomo (1986) found increased organic-C content in no-tillage compared with conventional tillage using hairy-vetch green manure.

A compilation of results by many authors is given in Table 16, in an attempt both to assess and compare the build-up of organic C and N in the soil under different crop/climate regimes and various durations. Singh (1967), Singh and Verma (1969) and Maurya and Ghosh (1972) observed no appreciable increase in organic C and N contents in green-manured plots over those receiving inorganic fertilizers. The effect of time, however, is more difficult to interpret, and further research is needed into the dynamics of equilibrium attainment over the medium short-term.

ELECTRO-CHEMICAL AND CHEMICAL PROPERTIES

Soil pH

According to Motomura (1962) green manuring decreases soil pH by producing organic acids and CO_2 during decomposition. Organic reducing substances formed during decomposition may, however, reduce Fe/Mn oxides thereby causing soil pH to rise (Ponnamperuma 1965). Green manuring may also result in increased soil pH through mineralization of organic anions to CO_2 and H_2O. Flooding tends

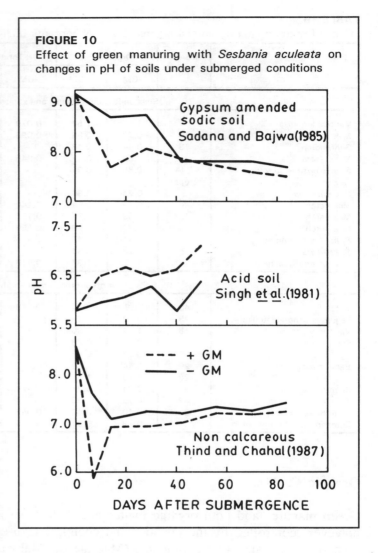

FIGURE 10

Effect of green manuring with *Sesbania aculeata* on changes in pH of soils under submerged conditions

to increase and decrease soil pH in acid and alkaline soils, respectively, leading to a steady state of near neutrality — the commonly observed effect of submerging a soil. Application of green manure therefore hastens the attainment of a steady pH state. As shown in Figure 10, application of sesbania green manure to gypsum-amended sodic soil, acid and non-calcareous soil helped in rapidly achieving near-neutral soil pH. Similar effects of green manuring with gliricidia have been reported by Katyal (1977) in black clay (pH 7.8), lateritic loam (pH 6.4) and red sandy loam pH (7.5) soils. More notably, in alkaline soils, pH dropped by almost 1 to 2 units during the first week of flooding following green manuring. After the initial sudden drop, the pH increased and attained more or less steady values after 4 weeks. Under aerobic soil conditions Bajpai *et al.* (1980) reported that green manuring with sesbania in a loam soil (pH 7.2) reduced pH after 2 weeks of incubation, but in a saline sodic clay loam soil (pH 9.9) a similar result was delayed for one month.

Kute and Mann (1968) reported no change with green manuring alone, but when applied with P a decline in soil pH was observed. Swarup (1987) also found a decrease in soil pH of a sodic soil by 0.2 units after a rice crop had been green-manured with sesbania. In a long-term experiment over 10 years, Sahu and Nayak (1971) observed no significant change in soil pH over the control due to green manuring in rice. Morachen *et al.* (1972) reported that green-manuring maize for 3 years with alfalfa residues at 16 t/ha reduced the soil pH from 5.3 to 5.1. Maurya and Ghosh (1972) also observed a decrease in soil pH, by 0.3 to 0.4 units, by green-manuring maize with sunn hemp for four years.

Changes in soil pH due to green manuring are complex and dependent on soil type and conditions, but in general, it has an overall tendency to move and buffer pH towards neutrality.

Redox Potential and Partial Pressure of CO_2

Redox potential (Eh) is very closely linked to the O_2-status of soils. Green manuring is not likely to have any significant effect on Eh levels of aerobic soils because CO_2 evolved during its microbial decomposition will diffuse relatively quickly when the soil-air spaces are large. However, the addition of green manure to waterlogged soils will enhance

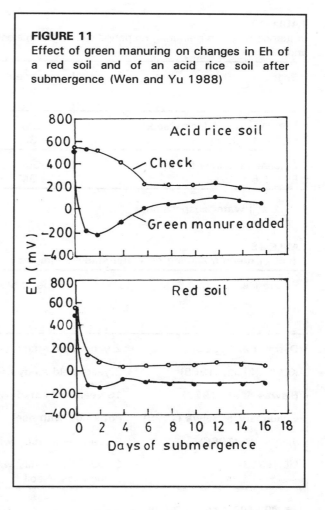

FIGURE 11

Effect of green manuring on changes in Eh of a red soil and of an acid rice soil after submergence (Wen and Yu 1988)

the rate of O_2 consumption (microbiological respiration and chemical oxidation of organic-reducing substances) resulting in CO_2 accumulation leading to a lower Eh potential.

Several studies have shown that green manures markedly reduce the Eh of waterlogged soils of differing pH, organic matter and easily-reducible Fe and Mn contents (Katyal 1977; Thind and Chahal 1983; Sadana and Bajwa 1985; Khind *et al.* 1987a). Figure 11 shows that in an acid soil with a very low organic matter content, Eh remained higher than 200 mV for several days of submergence, but with green manure application it dropped suddenly to as low as -200 mV within one to two days of flooding (Wen and Yu 1988). Katyal (1977) observed that depression in Eh due to green manuring was greater in black clay soil, which contained smaller amounts of reducible Fe and Mn, than in laterite or red soils.

Green manuring affects the rate of formation and the thickness of the oxidized layer in submerged soils. The latter ranges from 0.1 mm to more than 10 mm depending on soil conditions. When the amount of easily-decomposable organic matter is high, the thickness of the oxidizing layer will be small. Yu (1985) reported that application of green manure to a sandy soil reduced the thickness of the oxidized layer from 6 mm to 3 mm. The Eh of the oxidized and reduced layers was 225 and -79 mV, respectively, compared with 320 and 68 mV for no-green-manure treatment.

TABLE 17
Influence of green manuring on periodic changes in electrical conductivity (dS/m) of soil solution (Thind and Chahal 1987)

Soil	Treatment	Weeks of submergence				
		1	2	4	8	12
Non-calcareous loamy sand EC* 0.17 dS/m	-GM	1.15	0.97	0.80	0.80	0.70
	+GM	3.85	3.70	2.75	1.82	1.10
Calcareous sandy loam EC* 1.60 dS/m	-GM	2.50	2.30	2.20	2.00	1.55
	+GM	3.85	3.45	3.00	2.50	1.85

* 1:2 soil water suspension

TABLE 18
Effect of green manuring on water-stable aggregates

Reference	Type of study	Percentage of water-stable aggregates > 0.25 mm	
		-GM	+GM
Darra *et al.* (1968)	2 years field study on wheat	9.0	15.3
Kute & Mann (1968)	2 years field study on wheat	8.5	12.4
Biswas *et al.* (1970)	13 years field study with rice	24.0	37.1
Chaudhary & Bajwa (1979)	Pot study with rice	4.5	13.7
Jiao *et al.* (1986)	3 years field study with rice	14.9[1]	48.1[1]
Liu (1988)	3 years field study with rice on saline coastal soil	1.3	4.8

[1] = aggregate size 1-5 mm

Depletion of O_2 and accumulation of CO_2 is faster in waterlogged than in aerobic soils. Katyal (1977) observed higher and sharper peaks of Pco_2 in soil amended with green manure. Sadana and Bajwa (1985), in a laboratory study with salt-affected soil, also found a marked increase in Pco_2 with the addition of green manure. The difference of Pco_2 persisted over a 12-week period. High Pco_2 may increase the water-soluble Fe to a toxic amount, or HCO_3^- may directly poison the rice plant (Katyal 1977).

Electrical Conductivity

Electrical conductivity (EC) reflects the overall concentration of ions in the soil solution. Very few investigations have been made to study the effect of green manuring on electrical conductivity of upland soil. Under waterlogged conditions, the EC of the soil solution increases with time, reaches a peak and then decreases. The rise in EC is related to increase in the amounts of NH_4^+, Na^+, K^+, Fe^{2+}, Mn^{2+}, Ca^{2+} and Mg^{2+} ions (Ponnamperuma 1976), and decomposition of organic matter in the soil. The decrease in EC after an initial rise may be due to precipitation of Ca^{2+} and Mg^{2+} and consequent adsorption of other cations on the exchange sites, decrease in Pco_2 and decomposition of organic acids (Ponnamperuma 1972).

Katyal (1977) reported that application of gliricidia green manure to red, black and alluvial soils caused a sharp increase in EC within 14 days of flooding, followed by a rapid asymptotic decline up to 28 days. Sadana and Bajwa (1986) and Thind and Chahal (1987) observed a marked increase in EC of flooded soils amended with the green manure. The increase was more in non-calcareous than in calcareous soils (Table 17), and could be explained by greater release of Fe^{2+} and Mn^{2+} ions in the former soil.

PHYSICAL PROPERTIES

Green manuring improves several soil physical characteristics through addition of organic matter, and encourages *inter alia* ramification and proliferation of crop roots. The physical properties most commonly affected by green manuring are aggregation, bulk density, porosity, water retention and water transmission.

Aggregation

Many field and laboratory studies have shown that application of green manure to the soil appreciably increases the number and size of water-stable aggregates under both upland and wetland ecosystems. Representative results are given in Table 18.

Shinde and Sen (1958) reported that the average contents of water-stable aggregates (1.0-3.0 mm) in wheat plots were 4.4, 7.1 and 9.9 percent in control, green manure alone and green manure plus 26.2 kg P/ha, respectively. Ram and Zwerman (1960) found over 30 percent increase in soil aggregates (>0.5 mm) with green manuring. Miller and Kemper (1962) reported that the quantity of water-stable aggregates increased within a few weeks following incorporation of alfalfa residue, but decreased after one growing season. In a simulated tropical environment, Yaacob and Blair (1981) reported that in a granite soil, proportions of water-stable aggregates > 2 mm were 39.4 percent after incorporation of residues from one soybean crop, and 77.1 percent when six crops had been grown.

In a laboratory study, Rennie *et al.* (1954) found that more-readily decomposable legumes produced more stable aggregates in the short term, but that non-leguminous plant material produced longer-lasting effects. MacRae and Mehyus (1985) reported that the effects of green manures vary with soil texture and species used, and that the effects do not last long unless continuous additions are made. Silt-loam soils seem to be the most likely to show increases in aggregate stability from green manuring, with effects being more variable in clayey and sandy soil (Browning and Milam 1944; Chester *et al.* 1957; Wisniewski *et al.* 1958; Ram and Zwerman 1960). Allison (1968) stated that the direct effect of incorporated organic matter on aggregation is small and short-lived. The benefit is obtained from the cementing action on soil particles of microbial cells and polysaccharides released during decomposition of the organic matter.

Bulk Density

Organic matter, whether or not originating as leguminous green material, exerts a favourable influence on soil condition by lowering bulk density, as reported by several authors (Table 19), and consequently increasing porosity.

Obenshain and Gish (1941) reported that plough-down legume winter crops resulted in greater plasticity and lower bulk density than winter fallow. Bowren and McNaughton (1967) and Hageman and Shrader (1979), however, found no significant differences in bulk density after 20-28 years cropping using leguminous green manures. Neither did Mortensen and Young (1960) find any relationship between bulk density effects and aggregate stability owing to green manure treatments.

Bulk density is clearly dependent on other factors such as soil type, climate and time scale, and in any case appears to be related to an improved aggregation due to green manuring (Ram and Zwerman 1960; Benoit *et al.* 1962; Jiao *et al.* 1986; Liu 1988; Darra *et al.* 1968; Biswas *et al.* 1970).

Water Retention

Improvements in water-holding capacity of the soil due to green manuring have been reported by various workers (Table 20). Kang *et al.* (1985) reported that repeated application of leucaena prunings increased the moisture-retention capacity of sandy-loam soil. Joshi *et al.* (1990) found that after harvesting rice, when the free water had been withdrawn, plots treated with sesbania green manure retained 4 percent more water in the top 30 cm soil than plots receiving inorganic fertilizers. Evidence suggests that lighter soils cultivated aerobically are the more likely to benefit from green manuring in terms of water-holding capacity, bulk density and porosity than clayer soils, possibly because of their already high moisture-retention capacity.

Water Transmission

Green manuring has been reported by several authors to improve soil water-transmission properties such as hydraulic conductivity, infiltration rate, drainage capacity and porosity (Table 21).

Biswas *et al.* (1970) found that increase in hydraulic conductivity with green manuring was significantly and positively correlated with aggregate stability. Benoit *et al.* (1962) reported that increase in hydraulic conductivity is usually accompanied by a decrease in bulk density and increase in total porosity.

TABLE 19

Effect of green manuring on soil bulk density

Reference	Treatment	
	-GM	+GM
Ram & Zwerman (1960)	1.3	1.1
Darra *et al.* (1968)	1.46	1.36
Morachan *et al.* (1972)	1.10	1.04
Gu & Wen (1981)	1.23	1.11
Touchton *et al.* (1984)	1.95	1.82
Jiao *et al.* (1986)	1.39	1.31
Liu (1988)	1.46	1.33

TABLE 20

Effect of green manuring on water-holding capacity and available water in soil

Reference	Treatment	
	-GM	+GM
% water-holding capacity		
Darra *et al.* (1968)	35.0	37.2
Biswas *et al.* (1970)	13.9	16.4
Liu (1988)	43.6	46.5
% plant available water		
Biswas *et al.* (1970)	10.0	11.8

TABLE 21
Effect of green manure on hydraulic conductivity and infiltration rate of various soils

	Treatment		Reference
	-GM	+GM	
Hydraulic conductivity (cm/h)			
Sandy loam	0.65	2.43	Benoit *et al.* (1962)
Rice soil	0.25	0.29	Biswas *et al.* (1970)
Sodic soil	0.49	0.65	Chaudhary & Bajwa (1979)
Permeability (mm/h)			
Clay loam	0.27	0.91	Darra *et al.* (1968)
Drainage capacity (mm)	14.0	19.6	Liu (1988)
Infiltration rate (mm/h) 0-3 h			
Light-medium loam	30.0	42.7	Tejwani *et al.* 1966

Jen *et al.* (1965) found that green manuring increased soil porosity and promoted aggregation. Darra *et al.* (1968) also found that green manuring increased total porosity of soil, from 43.9 percent in unamended to 45.8 percent in green-manured plots. Liu (1988) reported that total- and non-capillary porosity were increased from 36.5 and 8.8 percent in no-green-manure plots to 45.9 and 10.9 percent in green-manured plots, respectively.

Yaacob and Blair (1981) reported a beneficial effect of incorporating soybean residues on the infiltration rate of the soil; an initial rate (0-5 min) increased from 8.1 mm/min after one crop to 13.4 mm/min after six crops. Touchton *et al.* (1984) recorded faster infiltration on plots carrying hairy vetch and crimson clover compared with fallow. In Africa, 2-3 years of legume cover increased infiltration rate and porosity of an eroded soil with initially poor physical properties (Wilson *et al.* 1982). However, Brown *et al.* (1985) found no significant difference in infiltration rate for hairy vetch or crimson clover covers versus winter fallow in no-tillage cotton. Gu and Wen (1981) stated that three annual applications of green manure did not improve the permeability of poorly-drained paddy soil, i.e. capillary porosity, although it increased total porosity of the soil.

Since an important objective in puddling wet-rice soil is to retain surface water, efforts to increase its permeability would be counter-productive. This is a special case, however, and the importance of increasing internal movement of water in the soil under aerobic cropping conditions is undeniable. Green manuring clearly achieves this purpose, albeit over the short term, primarily by improving soil-aggregating properties.

Soil Erodibility

In addition to the favourable effects reported above that green manuring has on soil stability and water acceptance — all factors affecting soil erodibility — a green-manure cover dissipates the energy of rain drops, protects the soil surface and reduces the velocity of moving rain water over the surface. This effect is especially important in annually-cropped areas with sloping terrain.

In the United States, several workers have reported favourable effects of winter-legume cover crops, e.g. hairy vetch, on soil erosion (Smith *et al*. 1987, Hargrove *et al*. 1984; Frye *et al*. 1985). Hale *et al*. (1984) observed that with no-tillage plus a crown-vetch cover crop, average annual run-off amounted to 0.21 cm compared with 5.71 cm for conventional tillage, and soil losses were 0.02 and 14.22 t/ha respectively. Frye *et al*. (1985) reported that the use of green-manure cover crops with no-tillage would allow maize to be grown on soil with slopes up to 20 percent, while keeping erosion below the tolerance limit. Smith *et al*. (1987) considered that the erosion control provided by short-term winter cover crops (effectively green manures) in the southeast United States, compared with bare fallow, was equal to or even greater than any other advantage.

In India, Tejwani *et al*. (1966) reported that in sloping tobacco fields subject to erosion during the rainy season, sunn hemp reduced run-off from 8.34 cm with no cover crop to 4.51 cm, and soil loss from 0.23 t/ha to 0.01 t/ha, respectively. Metzner (1982), Kabeerathumma *et al*. (1985), O'Sullivan (1985) and Kang and Wilson (1987) also reported a notable reduction in run-off and soil erosion when leucaena was included in the cropping system.

A short-term green-manure crop clearly has a directly beneficial effect on soil erosion during its growing period, but its effect after incorporation is the more relevant and quantifiable. A fuller discussion of the anti-erosion properties of long-term leguminous and non-leguminous cover crops lies more strictly in the domain of permanent cover crops, and is outside the scope of this publication.

Chapter 6

Reclamation of salt-affected soils

Green manuring has long been recognized as a useful practice for reclaiming saline and sodic soils. Incorporating a salt-tolerant green manure crop brings about favourable changes in the physico-chemical properties of such soils.

SALT-TOLERANCE OF GREEN MANURES

Plants differ in their capacity to tolerate salinity and sodicity in soils. Studies at the Central Soil Salinity Research Institute, Karnal, India (CSSRI 1979), showed that *Sesbania* spp. were the most successful green manures in salt-affected soils. Evans and Rotar (1987a) reported that sesbania (*S.aculeata*) withstands drought and waterlogging better than any other green-manure species, and is particularly well-suited to sodic soils. Uppal (1955) found that it produced twice as much green material as clusterbean (guar) or sunn hemp in high-pH sodic soils, but that leaching was helpful for its germination and establishment. Transplanted sesbania seedlings even withstood a soil pH above 9.5. Keating and Fisher (1985) found that yield reductions of 50 percent were associated with ECe 13.2 dS/m for sesbania , compared with lower ECe values for clusterbean (9.0 to 10.1), cowpea (9.0), soybean (6.7) pigeonpea and black gram (4.9 to 5.4), and green gram (3.5). Dargan *et al.* (1982) also reported that sesbania was tolerant to salinity. Uppal *et al.* (1961) found that while sesbania was highly salt-tolerant, pulses and sunn hemp were sensitive to soil salinity. Singhbutra *et al.* (1987), however, found that as salinity increased, plant height, biomass and nodule number decreased in *S. speciosa* and sesbania. Khan and Awan (1968) reported a sesbania crop that was either luxuriant, or had failed, where total soluble salts in the upper 23 cm soil horizon were 0.43 and 3.15 percent, respectively (the higher salt levels being due to abundance of NaCl and Na_2SO_4).

Swarup (1986, 1987) found that in sodic soils, increasing ESP (exchangeable-sodium percentage) from 16 to 32 had no significant effect on biomass and N-yield of sesbania; only at an ESP of 42, were adverse effects observed. In a study on the tolerance of 10 legumes to various levels of ESP (10 to 70), it was found that sesbania was relatively more sensitive to exchangeable-Na at germination, but once established, it grew even at high (over 50) ESP levels (CSSRI, 1979) (Figure 12).

Jen *et al.* (1965) reported that *S. aegyptiaca* (= *S.sesban*) tolerated salt concentrations from 0.42 to 1.04 percent in the seedling stage and from 0.92 to 1.39 percent as it reached maturity. Arshad and Hussain (1984) found that germination of *S. sesban* was satisfactory in an adjusted range of soil ECe from 1 to 8 dS/m. In solution culture (pH 6.5), *S. sesban*

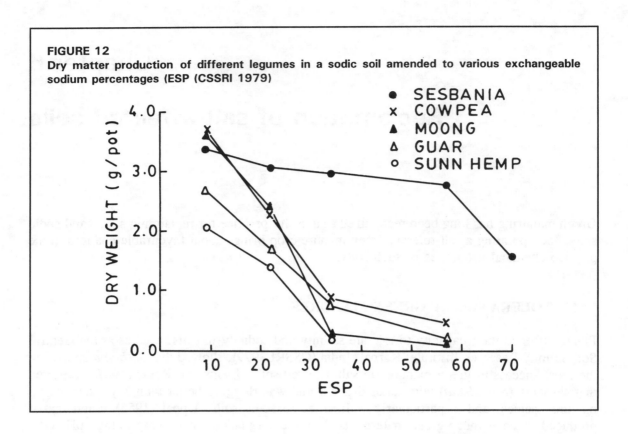

FIGURE 12
Dry matter production of different legumes in a sodic soil amended to various exchangeable sodium percentages (ESP (CSSRI 1979)

exhibited some mortality at a high level of salinity (200 m$\underline{M}$ NaCl) (Hansen and Munns 1985). Ghai *et al.* (1985) studied the effect of different salinity and alkalinity levels on the germination of three perennial sesbanias. The results indicated that *S. grandiflora* was the most sensitive to salinity and alkalinity at seed germination, whereas *S. aegyptiaca* and *S. glabra* were tolerant. *S. aegyptiaca* tolerated salinity stress better, while *S. glabra* performed well under alkaline conditions. Sinha (1982) reported that germination of *S. sesban* was inversely related to increasing salinity and alkalinity levels. Ahmad and Niazi (1977) reported that *S. sesban* was less tolerant of saline irrigation water (3.5 g salts/l) than clusterbean.

In some situations, soil amendment may be required before a green-manure crop can be grown. For example, Abrol and Bhumbla (1971) obtained low yields (2.1 t/ha fresh biomass) of sesbania on a saline-sodic soil, but with gypsum applications of 7.5 and 15 t/ha, yields increased to 16.1 and 17.4 t/ha, respectively. Dutt *et al.* (1983) reported that growth of *S. sesban* seedlings was almost doubled when soil pH was reduced from 8.4 to 7.9 by sulphur application. Poonia and Bhumbla (1972, 1973c) reported that sesbania dry-matter yields decreased considerably as soil ESP increased from 2 to 77, but with increasing rates of applied gypsum (2 to 8 me/100g saline-sodic soil) the dry-matter yields increased (Poonia and Bhumbla 1973a, b). Abrol and Bhumbla (1979) reported that when grown for 70 days without gypsum, sesbania yield was negligible on sodic soils, but application of 7.5 t/ha of gypsum maintained yields at 40 to 47 t/ha fresh biomass, over a soil ESP range of 10 to 50.

In pot studies, Poonia and Jhorar (1974) found that sesbania translocated relatively less absorbed Na to above-ground plant parts. This implies that incorporating sesbania tops as green manure will have a favourable effect on the salt balance of the soil.

Gillet (1963) and Char (1983) suggested that some species of sesbania may be obligate halophytes, while others such as *S. sesban* and *S. aculeata* may owe their wide distribution to a facultative tolerance of salt-affected conditions. Whatever the reason, numerous studies have shown that *S. aculeata*, and possibly also *S. speciosa* according to Whyte *et al.* (1953), are the species most suitable, at least under Indian conditions, for growing in high-pH and salt-affected soils with a view to improving them. Nevertheless, the work of Singh and Rai (1974) confirms that increasing levels of alkalinity and salinity result in decreased germination, root and shoot growth, nodulation and N_2 fixation of many legumes including sesbania. Furthermore, sodic (alkaline) conditions are more detrimental to important growth parameters than are saline conditions.

EFFECT ON BASE-EXCHANGE

Jen *et al.* (1965) reported that a dense plant cover of sesbania green manure reduces soil-water evaporation, thereby reducing the upward movement of salts and their concentration at the soil surface. In addition, and more importantly, the decomposition of green manure brings about favourable changes in the physico-chemical properties of salt-affected soils, and also supplies plant nutrients. The reclamation of sodic soils basically involves the replacement of Na ions on the exchange complex with more desirable Ca ions. An increase in CO_2 production in the soil following the incorporation of readily-decomposable plant material through green manuring — as observed by Katyal (1977), Bhardwaj and Dev (1985) and Beri *et al.* (1989a) — enhances the solubility of Ca in the soil. This in turn helps replace exchangeable Na resulting in an improved soil structure.

Singh (1969, 1974) also stated that CO_2 and organic acids produced during decomposition of green manure enhanced removal of exchangeable Na from sodic soils under saturated conditions. In a calcareous sodic soil, incorporation of sesbania plant material reduced an initial ESP from 91.3 to 28.4 over an 8-week incubation period and pH from 9.5 to 8.3, thus achieving a marked improvement in the physical condition of the soil.

Addition of green manure further contributes to the well-known effect of gypsum in improving the physico-chemical properties of the soil (Yadav and Agarwal 1961; Singh 1969, 1974; Sadana and Bajwa 1986). Yadav and Agarwal (1959) reported that green manuring together with gypsum favourably affected the structure of sodic soils and, therefore, their hydraulic conductivity, resulting in leaching of displaced sodium ions into deeper layers of the soil. Chaudhary and Bajwa (1979) also observed an increase in hydraulic conductivity in a sodic soil. Yadav and Agarwal (1961) observed greater improvement in the physico-chemical conditions of the soil with the application of gypsum (7.5 t/ha) and sesbania green manure as compared with gypsum alone (Table 22). The effects were more apparent after the second year, showing increasing levels of soil-N and organic matter.

In a field experiment, Swarup (1988) reported that application of gypsum (20 t/ha) together with green manure to a sodic soil resulted in a marked reduction in soil pH and ESP over application of gypsum alone (Table 23).

An indication has been given above of the quantitative improvement attainable in salt-affected soils by the use of green manure with and without a gypsum supplement. In practice, the economics of the operation will be the determining factor. This will depend upon (a) the

TABLE 22
Effect of gypsum and green manuring on physico-chemical properties of a sodic soil
(Yadav and Agarwal 1961)

Treatment		pH	$EC_e \times 10^3$ dS/m	Total anions me/100 g	ESP	Organic C (%)	Total N (%)	Permea-bility (cm/h)
Initial		10.2	18.99	9.81	51.9	0.25	0.04	0.50
After 1 year	-GM	8.7	3.57	1.85	5.38	0.33	0.06	2.08
	+GM	8.6	1.75	1.80	4.45	0.34	0.06	2.55
After 2 years	-GM	8.6	1.65	0.86	4.84	0.36	0.05	2.68
	+GM	8.5	1.42	0.84	4.21	0.53	0.09	4.20

TABLE 23
Effect of green manuring (GM) on soil pH and exchangeable sodium percentage (ESP) (0-15 cm soil depth) (Swarup 1988)

Treatment	At rice transplanting		After rice harvest	
	pH	ESP	pH	ESP
Without GM + 20 t/ha gypsum	9.6	45	9.4	36
With GM + 20 t/ha gypsum	9.3	35	9.0	30
CD at 5%	0.2	3	0.2	2
Initial	10.3	86.4		

TABLE 24
Response of rice to green manuring (GM) on salt-affected soils in India

Treatment	Rice grain yield (t/ha)		% increase
	-GM	+GM	
Uppal (1955)	1.42	3.15	122
Kirshna Rao & Raja Rao (1960)	1.47	2.14	46
Yadav & Agarwal (1961)			
1st year	1.26	1.44	14
2nd year	1.89	2.47	31
Dargan et al. (1975)[a]	4.74	6.63	40
Swarup (1987)[b]	5.35	6.79	27

[a] Mean yield under different N levels
[b] 150 kg N/ha as urea applied as a basal dressing

expected return in terms of crop response, (b) the degree of salinity/sodicity encountered, and (c) the longevity of the effect bearing in mind that that of the gypsum will be the greater.

INFLUENCE ON CROP YIELDS

Many research workers in India have reported considerable increases in rice yield with green manuring on saline and sodic soils. Typical results are quoted below and listed in Table 24. The favourable effects of green manuring on rice yields can be attributed to reduction in soil sodicity and salinity, and enhanced availability of nutrients especially N, P, Fe, Mn and Zn (Swarup 1987). In Thailand, growing and incorporating *S. speciosa* in sodic soils gave rice yields of 1.25 t/ha compared with 0.4 t/ha for no green-manure treatment (Arunin *et al.* 1987). Singh (1959) obtained more than 200 percent increase in rice yield with sesbania green manure at 30 t/ha. Krishna Rao and Raja Rao (1960) found that sesbania green manure was very effective in increasing rice yields on coastal saline soils in Andhra Pradesh (India). Sanyasi Raju and Govinda Iyer (1955) reported that leaching, accompanied by the application of 5 t/ha green-leaf manure, is the usual practice for correcting alkali conditions in Tamil Nadu. Mathur *et al.* (1973) reported significant rice-yield increases resulting from green manuring of salt-affected soils in Rajasthan (India).

The application of cattle manure as a treatment for salt-affected soils is a very old practice in India (Mann and Tamhane 1910). Yadav (1975) observed improvement of such soils through use of several organic amendments: farmyard manure, molasses, press-mud, green manure, crop residues and weeds, particularly *Argemone mexicana*. Use of weeds such as *A. mexicana* and *Ipomoea grandiflora*, and tree leaves were found equally satisfactory in ameliorating salt-affected soils (Dhawan *et al.* 1958; Chandra *et al.* 1961; Satyanarayana *et al.* 1961; Goel and Verma 1970).

Combinations of green manuring and gypsum, sulphur, lignite fly-ash, press-mud or pyrites amendments resulted in increases in rice yield on salt-affected soils (Dhawan *et al.* 1961; Mendiratta *et al.* 1972; Mahalingam 1973; Shetty 1975; Jauhari and Verma 1981; Somani and Saxena 1981). In addition, Shirwal and Deshpande (1977) demonstrated that fertilizers alone could not solve problems brought about by soil sodicity. Rice grown with

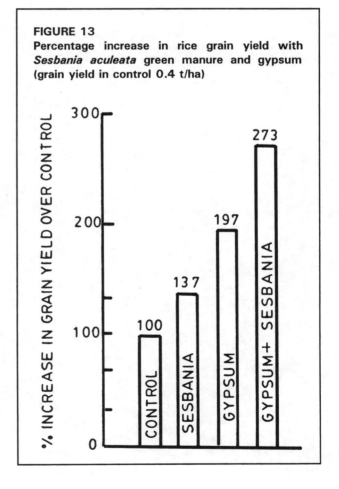

FIGURE 13
Percentage increase in rice grain yield with *Sesbania aculeata* green manure and gypsum (grain yield in control 0.4 t/ha)

N-P-K alone yielded 0.92 t/ha, but with the addition of 2.5 t/ha gypsum and green manuring with sesbania, yield increased to 3.7 t/ha. Misra (1976) using sesbania green manure, or farmyard manure incorporated at 5.6 t/ha, or gypsum at 12 t/ha on a salt-affected soil obtained increased rice yields of 57, 53 and 23 percent respectively, indicating that addition of organic matter was important for reclamation of those soils, and that gypsum alone was sometimes not as effective as organic matter. Agarwal (1957) demonstrated that rice-yield increases of 37 percent could be obtained using green manure alone, of 97 percent using gypsum, and of 173 percent using both treatments. Agarwal *et al*. (1950) compiled the results of 11 green-manure experiments on farmers' fields in Figure 13 (Agarwal *et al*. 1950), which typifies the beneficial effect of sesbania green manure complemented by gypsum on rice yields in salt-affected soils.

The responses of several major crops to green manuring under normal soil conditions are presented in the following section.

Chapter 7
Responses of crops to green manuring

RICE

In situ Green Manuring

Copious literature exists on the effect of green manuring on the grain yield of wetland rice. The major effect is undoubtedly due to the N contribution, but the favourable effects of organic matter addition and mobilization of other nutrients cannot be overlooked. Yield responses of wetland rice to green manuring in normal soils are reviewed below on a country-wise basis.

India

The work of Sethi *et al.* (1952) as reported by Staker (1958) showed that green manuring with sesbania and sunn hemp increased rice yield by 2 to 114 percent. The responses were small to negative in areas where soil water was insufficient. Panse *et al.* (1965) reviewed research on green manuring of indigenous tall rice cultivars with low yield potential. In 583 experiments conducted in 11 States covering diverse agro-climatic conditions, the grain yield response to green-manure application at 5.6 t/ha ranged from 0.1 to 0.3 t/ha, with an average of 0.24 t/ha. Similar yield responses of rice to green manuring have been reported by Rao and Ghosh (1952), Staker (1958), Relwani and Ganguly (1958), Vachhani and Murty (1964) and Chela and Gill (1973). Responses were related to soil fertility, and the amount of biomass and N added, which themselves were determined by the age of the green-manure crop.

With the introduction in the 1960s of high-yielding, fertilizer-responsive cultivars and intensive cropping, the use of green manures diminished in favour of inorganic fertilizers. However, interest in green-manuring research has now been renewed. Table 25 exemplifies the grain-yield response of high-yielding rice cultivars to green manuring in India. Over two-fold responses up to 3.0 t/ha have been reported, and are generally higher than those recorded for indigenous rice cultivars.

China and Japan

Grain-yield responses of rice to milk-vetch green manuring are given in Table 26; they ranged from 0.4 to 1.9 t/ha, rather less than found in India. Gu and Wen (1981) reported that responses differed according to soil fertility level. Table 26 shows that in the low-fertility soils, rice yields increased by 78 percent compared with 22 percent in the high-fertility soils. Bin (1983) reported that in 588 experiments conducted in south China, the addition of 1 t/ha of fresh green matter increased rice grain yield by 28 to 80 kg/ha.

TABLE 25
Rice grain yield response to green manuring (GM) in India

Green-manure crop	Age (days)	Rice grain yield (t/ha)			Reference
		-GM	+GM	% increase	
S. aculeata	-	2.15	2.55	19	Sahu & Nayak (1971)
S. aculeata	66	2.64	5.64	114	Dargan et al. (1975)
S. aculeata/Sunn hemp	60	3.22	3.97	23	Bhardwaj et al. (1981)
S. aculeata	50	1.55	2.69	74	Tiwari et al. (1980)
S. aculeata	50	3.30	6.10	85	Ghai et al. (1985)
S. aculeata/Sunn hemp	56	2.62	3.68	41	Sharma & Mittra (1988)
S. aculeata	60	2.90	4.00	38	Ramaswamy et al. (1988)
S. aculeata	56	4.50	6.10	36	Antil et al. (1988)
S. aculeata/Sunn hemp/ cowpea	60	2.70	5.50	105	Beri et al. (1989a)
S. aculeata	60	2.70	5.80	115	Beri et al. (1989b)
S. rostrata/Sunn hemp	-	2.40	3.10	29	Rabindra et al. (1989)

TABLE 26
Rice grain yield response to milk vetch green manure in China and Japan

Treatment	Rice grain yield (t/ha)			Reference
	-GM	+GM	% increase	
22.5 t/ha (F)	2.30	4.20	83	Yamazaki (1959)
15.9 t/ha (F) high fertility soils (mean of 26 experiments)	4.21	5.12	22	Gu & Wen (1981)
16.5 t/ha (F) medium fertility soils (mean of 32 experiments)	2.21	3.32	50	
14.4 t/ha (F) low fertility soils (mean of 16 experiments)	1.48	2.64	78	
90 kg GM-N/ha	3.10	4.20	35	Jiao et al. (1986)
75 kg GM-N/ha	3.80	5.00	32	
Mean of 13 years	2.90	4.20	45	Ishikawa (1988)
Mean of 54 years	2.00	3.40	85	
3.7 t/ha (D)	5.70	6.80	19	Chen (1988) (experiments in different regions)
2.9 t/ha (D)	10.70	12.30	15	
2.7 t/ha (D)	10.10	11.90	18	
4.5 t/ha (D)	6.70	7.10	6	
3.0 t/ha (D)	5.10	5.50	8	
4.5 t/ha (D)	5.20	6.10	17	

F = fresh matter, D = dry matter

TABLE 27
Rice grain yield response to green manuring in the Philippines and Thailand

Green-manure crop	Age (days)	Rice grain yield (t/ha)			Reference
		-GM	+GM	% increase	
Philippines					
Cowpea/mungbean	40-45	2.10	4.10	95	Morris *et al.* (1986a)
S. rostrata	48	1.80	3.50	94	Morris *et al.* (1989)
S. cannabina	48	1.80	3.45	92	
	60	1.80	4.10	128	
Cowpea	45	3.30	4.40	33	John *et al.* (1989c)
Eight legumes	60	3.30	4.27	29	Meelu *et al.* (1992)
S. rostrata	56	5.0	6.8	36	Manguiat. *et al.* (1992)
S. rostrata					
wet season	44-47	4.6-4.9	6.0-6.3	29-30	Ventura *et al.* (1987)
dry season	57	4.0	5.6	40	
S. rostrata					
wet season	48	2.1	3.0	43	Furoc & Morris (1989)
	60	2.1	3.6	71	
S. rostrata					
wet season	49	3.5-4.9	4.9-6.5	33-40	Becker *et al.* (1990)
dry season	56	4.0-4.1	6.3-6.9	58-68	
A. afraspera					
wet season	49	3.5-4.9	5.2-6.5	40-49	
dry season	56	4.0-41	6.5-7.2	63-76	
Thailand					
S. speciosa	-	1.30	2.30	84	Swasdee *et al.* (1976)
S. aculeata	35	2.53	3.68	45	Arunin *et al.* (1982)
S. speciosa	-	2.00	2.48	24	Arunin *et al.* (1988)
S. rostrata	-	1.64	2.17	32	Herrera *et al.* (1989)

Philippines

The data given in Table 27 show that rice grain-yield response to green manuring ranged from 0.90 to 3.10 t/ha.

Thailand

Rice grain-yield increases with green manuring ranged from 0.48 to 1.15 t/ha over control (Table 27), lower than in the Philippines where other more advanced practices may be expected to operate under the influence of the International Rice Research Institute.

United States

Green manuring with purple vetch, adding 30-45 kg N/ha, increased rice yield over control by 0.93 to 1.90 t/ha (Table 28). Westcott and Mikkelson (1987) found that application of 120 kg N/ha through vetch green manuring increased rice yield by 2.4 t/ha (43.4 percent) over

TABLE 28
Rice grain yield response to green manuring in the USA, Africa, Sri Lanka and Pakistan

Green-manure crop	Age (days)	Rice grain yield (t/ha)			Reference
		-GM	+GM	% increase	
USA					
Purple vetch	-	2.46	3.39	38	Williams *et al.* (1957)
Purple vetch	-	3.00	4.90	63	Williams *et al.* (1972)
Senegal					
S. rostrata	-	2.30	4.50	96	Diack (1986)
A. afraspera/A. nilotica	49	4.83	8.86	84	Alazard & Becker (1987)
Cameroon					
Sesbania sp.	50% flowering	1.72	2.06	20	Roy *et al.* (1988)
Crotalaria caricia	50% flowering	3.00	3.60	20	
		4.72	6.76	43	
		1.10	1.60	45	
Sri Lanka					
S. sesban	84	1.96	3.96	102	Palm *et al.* (1988)
Pakistan					
S. aculeata	-	1.36	2.29	68	Bhatti *et al.* (1985)

control. However, Dabney *et al.* (1989) reported that green manuring with subterranean clover increased grain yield of rice by only about 10 percent in both tillage and no-tillage systems.

Senegal

Green manuring with stem-nodulating *Aeschynomene* spp. increased rice yield by 2.2 to 4.0 t/ha over control (Table 28). In a microplot study, Rinaudo *et al.* (1983) reported that green manuring with 52-day-old *S. rostrata* increased rice yield by 18% over no green manure.

Cameroon

Roy *et al.* (1988) reported increases in rice grain yield from green manuring with sesbania and sunn hemp ranging from 0.34 to 2.04 t/ha (Table 28).

Sri Lanka

Palm *et al.* (1988) observed that green manuring with 84-day-old *S. sesban* increased rice yield by 2 t/ha (Table 28).

Pakistan

Green manuring with *S. aculeata* increased rice grain yield by 0.93 t/ha over control, according to Bhatti *et al.* (1985) (Table 28).

Surinam

Crotalaria quinquifolia is reported by ten Have (1959) to be a promising green manure capable of increasing rice yields by 1.0 t/ha.

Australia

Chapman and Myers (1987) reported that green manuring increased rice grain yield by 0.6 t/ha.

The above brief review indicates the widespread and considerable nature of rice-yield response obtainable from green manures alone.

Green-leaf Manuring

The response to green-leaf manuring (GLM), as with *in situ* green manuring, is mainly due to N contribution, although the amounts added are less because that provided by the root-nodule system is missing. Nevertheless, considerable responses in rice yield have been reported. Krishna Rao *et al.* (1961) studied the effect of green-manuring rice with loppings of different quick-growing shrubs. The results showed that grain yield increased by 21 to 114 percent (mean 51 percent). Singh (1971) evaluated several different legumes growing in the wild and adding 35 t GLM/ha to wetland rice and recorded yield increases from 17 to 59 percent over no GLM treatment. *Tephrosia* spp. and *Aeschynomene americana* were the most efficient species, probably due to their greater succulence, N content and ability to decompose readily. Table 29 shows the grain-yield responses to GLM in various studies; they ranged from 0.3 to 3.9 t/ha. Maskey and Bhattarai (1984) used four different non-leguminous species adding 100 kg N/ha, which increased rice yield by 13 percent (with *Eupatorium gladiosa*) to 54 percent (with *Adhatoda vasica*). Preliminary studies in Sri Lanka showed that incorporation of 2.6 t/ha of leucaena loppings increased rice grain yield by 28 percent over the control (Weerakoon 1983).

The findings quoted above indicate the feasibility of using indigenous wild-growing leguminous or non-leguminous herbage, and that from alley- or hedge-row plantings, as green-manure material. Compared with straight-forward ploughing-in of the *in situ* material, however, the cutting, collecting, transporting and distributing over the field prior to incorporating the GLM considerably increases the labour demands of the system. The main advantage is that crop land and growing time are not being occupied by the production of the GLM.

Intercropping with Green Manures

A green-manure crop can be sown as an intercrop with rice when both are direct seeded. Vachhani and Murty (1964) reported that intercropping with sesbania increased rice grain yield by 16.3 percent, saving about 22.4 kg N/ha as ammonium sulphate. Panse *et al.* (1965)

TABLE 29
Response of rice to green-leaf manuring (GLM)

Green-leaf crop	Fresh biomass/N additions	Rice grain yield (t/ha)		Reference
		-GLM	+GLM	
Kakavati	10 t/ha	1.8	3.2	Hernandez *et al.* (1958)
Gliricidia maculata	-	2.2	3.0	Sahu (1965)
G. maculata	7.5 t/ha (57.8 kg N/ha)	2.1	3.5	Reddi *et al.* (1972)
G. maculata	9.0 t/ha	3.8	4.6	Nagarajah & Amarasiri (1977)
Tithonia diversifolia	9.0 t/ha	4.3	4.6	
L. leucocephala	120 kg N/ha flooded non-flooded	2.9 2.1	6.8 4.0	Laolao *et al.* (1978)
S. bispinosa + *Ipomoea carnea*	10 t/ha (dry matter)	4.0	5.3	Chatterjee *et al.* (1979)
Fertilizer	40 kg/ha	4.0	4.8	
L. leucocephala	5.6 t/ha	1.8	2.3	Weerakoon (1983)
I. carnea wet season dry season	25-40 kg N/ha 25-40 kg N/ha	3.2 3.2	4.7 3.8	Jha *et al.* (1980)
L. leucocephala	12.5 t/ha	4.0	4.9	Karuppiah & Thangamuthu (1986)
G. maculata	100 kg N/ha	2.3	4.3	Gopalaswamy & Vidhyasekarn (1987)
Pongamia glabra	100 kg N/ha		4.6	
Azadirchta indica	100 kg N/ha		4.9	
Aeschynomene indica	7.5 t/ha 16.9 t/ha 10.0 t/ha 15.0 t/ha	4.6 5.8 4.9 3.4	5.7 6.8 5.6 4.6	Liu (1988)
L. leucocephala	10 t/ha +50 kg N/ha + 75 kg N/ha	2.8 3.6 4.0	3.6 4.3 4.8	Jeyaraman & Purushothaman (1988)

TABLE 30
Effect of *Sesbania* intercropping on rice yield in China (Liu 1988)

Sesbania spacings (cm)	Fresh biomass (t/ha)	Rice yield (t/ha)		
		Early rice	Late rice	Total
600 x 25	6.0	6.0	5.6	11.6
400 x 25	8.6	5.8	5.7	11.5
260 x 25	11.5	5.6	5.9	11.5
Control	-	5.8	5.0	10.8

summarized the results from several studies on intercropping of sesbania, *S. speciosa*, sunn hemp and *Indigofera* green manure in rice. On average, the response, which varied considerably among the different studies, was only about 47 kg (6.5 percent) of rice grain/ha over control treatment. In some experiments green manuring had negative responses because of shortage of moisture for decomposing the green manure. Hati (1987) intercropped sesbania with upland rice for 20 days and then killed the green manure plants with propanil selective herbicide to avoid excessive competition. Sesbania increased rice grain yield by 0.3 t/ha (27 percent), resulting in a saving of about 40 kg fertilizer N/ha (see also section Nitrogen-recovery and fertilizer equivalence).

In studies in China reported by Liu (1988), sesbania seedlings were intercropped at spacings of 200-600 cm x 25 cm at about 30 days after transplanting rice. After the early (first crop) rice harvest the sesbania plants, which accumulated 7.5-12.0 t green biomass/ha, were incorporated as basal manure for the late (second crop) rice. Data presented in Table 30 show that although the early rice yielded less, the late-rice yield was increased by 12-20 percent and the total yields of both crops exceeded the control by 0.7-0.8 t/ha.

The advantage of intercropping is that no crop time is lost by growing the green manure separately. However, problems arise in incorporating it without unduly disturbing the developing rice crop, and possible competition for soil moisture in periods of shortage. It should be noted that, in many areas where rice is hand-weeded several times, the biomass of weeds is often buried simultaneously, thereby contributing organic matter and nutrients.

Dual-purpose Leguminous Green Manures

Legumes for grain and green manuring

Short-duration pulses such as mungbean and cowpea grown in the fallow period before transplanting rice provide much-needed protein for human consumption, and their residues can be turned under to serve as a green manure. Data given in Table 31 show that response of rice to dual-purpose legume green manures ranged from 0.3 to 1.1 t/ha. Xiao (1980) reported that incorporating a winter crop of beans (*Phaseolus vulgaris*) after pod harvest gave a 19 percent increase in the yield of the subsequent rice crop.

Further examples of the benefits of using dual-purpose green manures are given in the following section where N-fertilizer equivalence is discussed.

Legumes for forage and green manuring

The total productivity of the agricultural sectors of tropical and sub-tropical regions depends not only on food crops but also on livestock production. In Asia for example, over 60% of food is produced by small landholders who keep livestock in mixed crop/livestock farming systems (Moong 1986). The cereals straw and stover (rice, maize, wheat and sorghum) are the most important livestock feed and have very low feed value in such systems. There is a need to supplement straw and stover with forage legumes to improve the feeding value. As a result, the use of herbaceous forages and tree legumes (Annex I) is being increasingly advocated. In Asia, farm size is generally small and farmers' priority is food crops. Farmers do not generally grow forage crops by reducing the area under food crops. Recent studies in the Philippines have shown that for harnessing inter-row space in wide row crops there is

TABLE 31
Effect of legume residues on rice grain yield

Grain legume	Dry biomass/N added	Rice grain yield (t/ha)		Reference
		-GM	+GM	
Cowpea	-	2.8	3.2	Timsina (1981)
Mungbean	4.6 t/ha (101 kg N/ha) + 60 kg N/ha +120 kg N/ha	3.2 5.2 7.1	6.5 7.4 8.5	Rekhi & Meelu (1983)
Green gram	1.25 t/ha 2.50 t/ha	3.0 3.1	3.4 3.8	Gangwar & SIngh (1985)
Green gram	43 kg N/ha	2.9	3.2	Prasad & Palaniappan (1987)
Soybean	52 kg N/ha	3.3	3.8	
Cowpea	-	2.6	3.5	Kulkarni & Pandey (1988)
Cowpea	3.0 t/ha (44 kg N/ha)	3.3	4.4	John *et al.* (1989c)

TABLE 32
Grain and fodder dry matter yields of sorghum and forage crops, amount of green manure and weeds incorporated before transplanting rice and yields of rice under irrigated lowland ecosystem at IRRI, 1991 (Carangal *et al.* 1992)

Treatment	Sorghum yields (t/ha)		Forage crop DM fodder yield (t/ha)	DM biomass of green manure (t/ha)		Rice grain yield (t/ha)
	Grain	Fodder (main + ratoon)		Forage crop	Weeds	
Sorghum	4.4	9.3	-	-	0.38[b]	2.4[a]
Desmanthus	-	-	13.9[a]	7.4[a]	0.22[b]	4.8[c]
Sorghum + Desmanthus	4.2	7.5	7.6[c]	4.9[b]	0.30[b]	4.1[bc]
Clitoria	-	-	9.3[b]	3.6[bc]	1.19[ab]	4.8[c]
Sorghum + Clitoria	3.9	8.7	5.2[d]	2.1[d]	0.29[b]	3.8[bc]
Stylo	-	-	10.5[b]	4.8[b]	0.32[b]	3.6[abc]
Sorghum + Stylo	3.6	7.9	5.4[d]	2.7[cd]	0.53[b]	3.3[ab]
Fallow 30N	-	-	-	-	1.66[a]	2.9[ab]
Fallow 60N	-	-	-	-	2.03[a]	3.6[abc]
Fallow 90N	-	-	-	-	2.08[a]	3.8[bc]

potential to integrate forage crops in existing and improved cropping systems as intercrop and relay crops without reducing the area for food crops (Carangal *et al.* 1992). The scheme can produce food crops, animal feed and green manure for the succeeding crop.

Sorghum and forage crop intercropping: Carangal *et al.* (1992) intercropped sorghum with Clitoria (*Clitoria ternatea*), Desmanthus *(Desmanthus virgatus)* and Stylo *(Stylosanthes guianesis)*. Forage harvesting was done 60 to 90 days after seeding and subsequent cutting interval was 3-4 weeks. Desmanthus was harvested 6 times whereas Clitoria and Stylo were harvested 3 times. Sorghum was ratooned after harvesting the grain and allowed to grow for forage production until the land preparation for the following rice crop. The last herbage regrowth of the forage legumes was incorporated into the soil as green manure two weeks before transplanting the rice crop.

Sorghum grain and fodder dry matter yields were not significantly affected by intercropping (Table 32). Yields of monocropped forage crops were significantly higher than the intercrops in 7 months (December-June).

The highest grain yield of rice was obtained from plots previously planted to monocrops, Desmanthus and Clitoria and the lowest yield was recorded from sorghum-ratoon sorghum cropping pattern (Table 32). Rice yields from the monocrop forage legumes and sorghum intercropped with Desmanthus and Clitoria were similar to those with 90 kg N/ha fertilizer application on fallow plots.

Maize and forage crop intercropping: Hybrid maize was intercropped with Desmanthus, Clitoria and sunn hemp (Carangal *et al.* 1992). First cutting of forage legumes was 35 days after sowing for sunn hemp and 66 days for Desmanthus and Clitoria. Average cutting interval for forage legume was 21-23 days, 22 days (sunn hemp), 23 days (Clitoria) and 21 days (Desmanthus). The last forage crop regrowth was incorporated as green manure 2 weeks before transplanting rice. Grain and fodder yields of maize were not significantly affected by intercropping (Table 33). The yield of maize was low due to borer infestation. Therefore, yield of relayed mungbean was not significantly affected by the forage crops although the monocropped mungbean yielded higher than the intercrops. Forage yield of legumes was significantly reduced by maize.

Rice yield was significantly increased by the incorporated forage legumes used as green manure except in maize intercropped with sunn hemp (Table 33). Highest rice yield was obtained after monocrop Desmanthus. Forage green manures produced more rice yield than that with 90 kg N/ha applied on fallow plots and was at par with sunn hemp.

Pigeonpea and forage crop intercropping Pigeonpea is a promising drought-tolerant crop. Pigeonpea with no fertilizer application was intercropped with Siratro, sunn hemp, Clitoria and Desmanthus (Carangal *et al.* 1992). Pigeonpea was ratooned after harvesting the grain for animal feed. The ratooned crop regrowth was incorporated together with the last forage of legumes regrowth as green manure for the succeeding rice crop. The number of forage cuttings vary with 3 cuttings for Desmanthus, 2 for Siratro, 6 for sunn hemp and 3 for Clitoria.

Performance of pigeonpea was not significantly affected by intercropping of forage legumes with a mean grain yield of 1.1 t/ha, fodder yield of 0.6 t DM/ha and ratoon of

TABLE 33
Grain and fodder dry matter yields of hybrid maize, mungbean and forage crop, amount of green manure and weeds incorporated before transplanting rice and yields of rice under irrigated lowland ecosystem at IRRI 1991 (Carangal *et al.* 1992)

Treatment	Maize yield (t/ha)		Mungbean yield (t/ha)		Forage crop yield (t/ha)	DM biomass of green manure (t/ha)		Rice grain yield (t/ha)
	Grain	Fodder	Grain	Fodder		Forage crop	Weed	
Maize/mungbean	3.1	2.8	1.0	0.7[a]	-	-	1.7[a-d]	3.0[d]
Maize + Desmanthus/mungbean	2.8	2.6	0.7	0.4[b]	3.1[b]	5.4[b]	1.0[cde]	3.9[bc]
Desmanthus	-	-	-	-	5.8[a]	7.3[a]	0.2[e]	4.8[a]
Maize + Clitoria/mungbean	3.2	2.7	0.6	0.5[b]	3.0[b]	2.7[c]	1.2[bcd]	4.6[ab]
Clitoria	-	-	-	-	5.6[a]	2.8[c]	0.9[de]	4.5[ab]
Maize + Crotolaria/mungbean	2.9	2.3	0.6	0.6[b]	3.3[b]	3.9[bc]	1.4[a-d]	3.8[bcd]
Crotolaria	-	-	-	-	5.6[a]	4.5[bc]	1.0[cde]	4.4[ab]
Fallow 30N	-	-	-	-	-	-	2.0[abc]	3.2[cd]
Fallow 60N	-	-	-	-	-	-	2.2[ab]	3.5[cd]
Fallow 90N	-	-	-	-	-	-	2.3[a]	3.8[bc]

TABLE 34
Grain and fodder dry matter yields of pigeonpea and forage crops, amount of green manure and weeds incorporated before transplanting rice and yield of rice under rainfed lowland ecosystem at IRRI 1991 (Carangal *et al.* 1992)

Treatment	Pigeonpea yield (t/ha)		Forage crop fodder yield (t/ha)	DM biomass of green manure (t/ha)			Rice grain yield (t/ha)	
	Grain	Fodder		Pigeon pea	Forage crop	Weeds	+GM	-GM
Pigeonpea	1.3	0.8	-	5.4	-	0.9[bcd]	5.2[bc]	4.0
Crotalaria	-	-	4.4[a]	-	4.4[abc]	1.2[bc]	5.6[c]	3.9
Pigeonpea + Crotalaria	0.9	0.6	2.8[c]	4.1	1.9[cd]	0.6[cd]	5.5[c]	3.7
Clitoria	-	-	4.3[a]	-	4.1[abc]	0.5[cd]	5.2[bc]	4.5
Pigeonpea + Clitoria	0.7	0.5	2.6[c]	4.3	1.7[cd]	0.3[d]	4.9[bc]	4.2
Desmanthus	-	-	3.8[b]	-	6.1[a]	0.2[d]	5.1[bc]	3.9
Pigeonpea + Desmanthus	1.4	0.7	1.2[e]	5.0	2.4[bcd]	0.2[d]	5.2[bc]	3.6
Siratoro	-	-	1.7[d]	-	5.1[ab]	1.7[ab]	4.8[bc]	3.5
Pigeonpea + Siratoro	1.0	0.6	0.7[f]	5.1	0.9[d]	0.4[cs]	5.2[bc]	3.6
Fallow 0N	-	-	-	-	-	2.1[a]	2.8[a]	2.7
Fallow 25N	-	-	-	-	-	2.4[a]	4.1[b]	3.6
Fallow 50N	-	-	-	-	-	2.2[a]	4.5[bc]	4.5

4.8 t DM/ha (Table 34). Highest grain yield was observed in pigeonpea + Desmanthus combination with 1.4 t/ha compared to monocrop yield of 1.3 t/ha. Yields of monocrop forage legume were significantly higher than in intercropped systems due to thick canopy production of pigeonpea especially after ratoon.

Rice to which green manure was applied gave significantly higher yields than the rice without green manure application (above ground residue removed). However, when the above ground were removed (no green manure treatment), the plots previously planted with Clitoria as monocrop or intercropped with pigeonpea gave the highest rice grain yield of 4.5 t/ha, the same yield as the 50 kg N fertilizer application. Rice yields were not significantly different from plots previously planted with pigeonpea + forage legumes regardless of combinations and without green manure. The yield of rice in the fallow treatments applied with inorganic fertilizer at the rate of 25 kg N/ha (4.1 t/ha grain and 5.1 t/ha straw) and 50 kg N/ha (4.5 t/ha grain and 5.5 t/ha straw) were slightly lower than from any of the crop combinations with green manure in the study.

Rice-forage crop intercropping: Magbanua *et al.* (1991) studied the effect of inter/relay planting of forage legumes, Lablab (*Lablab purpureus*) and Sirato (*Macroptillium atropurpureum*) in wet season rice from 1987 to 1989. The excess vegetative growth of lablab and Sirato was clipped during rice growth seasons and one half/all was incorporated as green manure and the remaining half was removed as simulated forage for animals. Across years, the annual N additions from the lablab and Sirato ranged from 91 to 209 kg/ha more from the former compared to latter legume. Grain yield differences in treatments with and without forage legumes were significant in one out of three years and intercropped forage legumes increased rice yield up to 2 t/ha in that year. This suggests that with proper management of legume forage intercropping can improve upland rice yields and part of the forage can be used as food for animals.

Winter legumes for forage and green manure: In Minnesota, USA, Groya and Sheaffer (1985) studied harvest management of sweet clover (*Melilotus officinalis* (L.) Lam.), red clover (*Trifolium pretense* L.) and alfalfa (*Medicago sativa* L.) in terms of production of fodder and incorporation of a part of the herbage and roots as green manure for succeeding crop of Sudangrass (*Sorghum bicolor* L. Moench). Harvest management included: (i) herbage harvested as fodder and fall regrowth incorporated as green manure, (ii) herbage from both seeding year and fall regrowth harvested, only roots incorporated into soil, (iii) herbage from seeding year and fall regrowth incorporated as green manure and (iv) no harvest; accumulated herbage incorporated into soil. Legume N incorporated as green manure in the four systems ranged from 45 to 173, 36 to 112, 228 to 357 and 173 to 352 kg N/ha, respectively. Nitrogen uptake and dry matter yield of Sudangrass were significantly correlated to legume N incorporation in different harvest managements. Sudangrass dry matter yields from fallow treatments exceeded those from the treatment from which all herbage had been removed as fodder.

Nitrogen Recovery and Fertilizer Equivalence

The N-contribution from green manures is the most commonly observed and economically important benefit in wetland rice production. Direct measurements of N recovered, i.e. N actually transferred from the green manure crop to the rice crop, are not easily made, and only limited data are available.

Recovery of green-manure N in rice has been found to vary considerably with legume species, soil type, management and weather. Table 35 shows that apparent green-manure N recoveries in different studies varied from 21 to 78 percent. In general, recoveries of N from green manure were similar to those from fertilizer. Working with a clay soil and using ^{15}N-labelled vetch green manure, Westcott and Mikkelson (1987) recorded 10 percent N-recovery of added vetch N (at 120 kg N/ha) and 23 percent with ammonium sulphate on an equivalent

TABLE 35
Recovery of green manure N by rice under different species and conditions

Green-manure crop	% N recovery		Reference
	GM	Fertilizer	
	Apparent N recovery		
Mungbean/cowpea	33-49	33-39	Morris *et al.* (1986b)
A. afraspera/A. nilotica	25-35	35	Alazard & Becker (1987)
S. aculeata	44	38	Ghai *et al.* (1988)
S. aculeata	42	50	Yadvinder-Singh *et al.* (1988a)
Cowpea	21-29	25-43	John *et al.* (1989c)
S. rostrata	41	34	Rabindra *et al.* (1989)
Sunn hemp	34	34	
S. rostrata	34-51	-	Ladha *et al.* (1989)
S. aculeata	58	61	Shukla *et al.* (1989)
S. rostrata			
wet season	23-39	45-50	Becker (1990)
dry season	47-78	43-54	
A. afraspera			
wet season	21-28	45-50	
dry season	38-52	43-54	
S. rostrata			
wet season	61-63	30-46	Ventura *et al.* (1987)
dry season	75	60	
	^{15}N recovery		
Milk vetch	25	-	Gu & Wen (1981)
Sesbania sp.	30-34	51-64	
Sunn hemp	34-45	57-60	Huang *et al.* (1981)
Milk vetch	38	-	Liu (1981)
Milk vetch	30	25	Mo & Qian (1983)
S. aculeata	32	51	Biswas (1988)
S. rostrata	42-49	23-31	Diekmann *et al.* (1991)
A. afraspera	40-47	23-31	

N basis. They observed that when conditions inhibited the early-season mineralization of green-manure N, recovery rates would not compare favourably with that of fertilizer N. On the other hand, Williams and Finfrock (1962) working with different soils and rice cultivars found apparent vetch-N recovery rates as high as 100 percent. Chapman and Myers (1987) indicated that inefficient management of green manure could result in its low efficiency in wetland rice.

Many studies provide an indirect measurement of N-contribution by comparing rice-yield response to N-fertilizer with and without green manures. The parameter nitrogen fertilizer equivalence (NFE) of a green manure in wetland rice is often calculated as the quantity of fertilizer N that must be applied to obtain grain yields equal to those obtained with green manure alone. This approach could at best be regarded as an approximation as the green manure effect is not from the N-contribution alone but from other factors as well.

The NFE values of different green manure crops in wetland rice from various studies are given in Table 36. These range from 34 to 148 kg N/ha, but more typically are between

TABLE 36
Nitrogen fertilizer equivalence (NFE) of green manure N in rice

Green-manure crop	Age (days)	Green manure N (kg/ha)	NFE (kg/ha)	Reference
Purple vetch	-	27-49	34	Williams *et al.* (1957)
Crotalaria quinquifolia	105	-	100	ten Have (1959)
S. aculeata	-	23	34	Vachhani & Murty (1964)
S. aculeata	67	-	80	Dargan *et al.* (1975)
S. aculeata	50	-	80	Tiwari *et al.* (1980)
S. aculeata	50	57	50	Bhardwaj *et al.* (1981)
Sunn hemp	50	78	75	
S. rostrata	52	-	130	Rinaudo *et al.* (1983)
S. cannabina	45-65	98-147	100-120	Bhardwah & Dev (1985)
S. rostrata	55	131	80	Crozat & Sangchyosawat (1985)
Milk vetch	-	90	90	Jiao *et al.* (1986)
Mungbean/cowpea	40-45	74-86	80	Morris *et al.* (1986a)
A. afraspera/A. nilotica	49	-	>100	Alazard & Becker (1987)
S. rostrata	50	-	70	Ventura *et al.* (1987)
S. aculeata	45	109	123	Ghai *et al.* (1988)
S. aculeata/sunn hemp	(a)	-	40-60	Roy *et al.* (1988)
Milk vetch	23.4 t/ha (b)	-	94	Ishikawa (1988)
S. sesban	84	83	96	Palm *et al.* (1988)
S. aculeata	56	98	45	Sharma & Mittra (1988)
Sunn hemp	56	149	60	
S. aculeata/sunn hemp/ cowpea	60	108-113	120	Beri *et al.* (1989a, b)
S. cannabina/cowpea/ sunn hemp	60	-	50-105	Meelu *et al.* (1992)
S. cannabina	48	-	80	Morris *et al.* (1989)
S. rostrata	-	70	70	Rabindra *et al.* (1989)
S. aculeata	60	-	90	Shukla *et al.* (1989)
S. aculeata	-	45-75	72	Yadvinder-Singh *et al.* (1990)
S. aculeata	-	97-150	136	
Sunn hemp	-	41-70	72	
Sunn hemp	-	121	148	
Cowpea	-	55-80	98	

(a) flowering
(b) green material

50 and 100 kg N/ha for 45- to 60-day-old green-manure crops. In a number of studies on an equal-N basis, the efficiency of the green manure was equal to or more than that of fertilizer N. Roger and Watanabe (1986) reported that incorporating one legume crop is equivalent to applying 30 to 80 kg fertilizer N/ha in rice. To increase precision of the estimate, some research workers (Ghai *et al.* 1988; Yadvinder-Singh *et al.* 1990) have used regression equations of the response to varying fertilizer-N levels for computing NFE of green manures.

Yamazaki (1959) showed that in wetland rice fields, yields from the plots green-manured with milk vetch were almost the same in well-drained soils, but less in medium or poorly-drained soils, compared with the yields from ammonium sulphate-fertilized plots.

TABLE 37
Rice grain yield response to fertilizer N and combined use of green manure (GM) and fertilizer N

Fertilizer N (kg/ha)	GM + fertilizer N (kg/ha)	Rice grain yield (t/ha)		N substitution with GM (kg/ha)	Reference
		Fert. N	GM + fert. N		
69 (+20P+17K)	40 (+11P+8K)	6.1	6.4	29 (+9P+9K)	Nagarajah & Amarasiri (1977)
94	38	4.0	4.2	56	Ishikawa (1988)
120	40	6.0	6.3	80	Dargan et al. (1975)
120	60	7.1	7.4	60	Rekhi & Meelu (1983)
70 (+15P+29K)	35 (+7.5P+14.5K)	4.1	4.2	35 (+7.5P+14.5K)	Joseph (1986)
120	30	6.2	5.9	90	Camara & Diara (1986)
120	40	5.0	4.9	80	Tiwari et al. (1980)
90	60	4.1	4.1	30	Roy et al. (1988)
90	60	5.2	5.2	30	
90	60	4.3	4.3	30	Sharma & Mittra (1988)
100	60	3.8	4.6	>40	Kalidurai & Kannaiyan (1990)
100	50	5.2	6.1	>50	Rabindra et al. (1989)
120	60	6.2	6.4	60	Beri & Meelu (1981)
135	90	6.4	6.3	45	Williams et al. (1972)
90	30	4.6	4.5	60	Bhardwaj et al. (1981)
150	100	6.6	6.5	50	Palaniappan & Srinivasulu (1990)

Krishna Rao *et al.* (1961) and Jiao *et al.* (1986) reported that green-manure N was as effective as fertilizer N when added on an equal-N basis. Antil *et al.* (1988) computed optimum N rates for wetland rice to be 152, 74 and 66 kg N/ha after fallow, *S. aculeata* and sunn hemp, respectively. John *et al.* (1989c) reported that cowpea on average yielded about 1 t/ha of peas and its residue, containing about 54 kg N/ha, gave rice yields equivalent to 44-50 kg fertilizer N/ha.

In a region where two rice crops are grown in a rotation, incorporating crop residues of short-duration grain legumes (mungbean, black gram, cowpea) substituted for 50 percent of fertilizer N in wet-season rice (Kulkarni and Pandey 1988). Gangwar and Singh (1985) observed that with incorporation of green-gram residues at 1.25 t/ha (one-half of the crop residue available) and 2.5 t/ha (full quantity), similar rice yields were given by applying 100 and 50 kg fertilizer N/ha, respectively. From a three-year study, Rekhi and Meelu (1983) reported that in addition to about 0.9 t grains/ha, mungbean residue supplied about 100 kg N/ha, and its combined use with 60 kg fertilizer N/ha gave rice yields comparable to 120 kg N/ha as urea. Gopalaswamy and Vidhyasekaran (1987) showed that at 100 kg N/ha, GLM and urea were equally efficient in increasing the grain yield of rice.

Chatterjee *et al.* (1979) reported that incorporating *Ipomoea carnea* and sesbania (10 t/ha, dry weight basis) yielded as much rice as did 40 kg N/ha (as urea) applied at transplanting. Jha *et al.* (1980) reported that rice grain yield with *I. carnea* GLM was comparable or even superior to that obtained with similar N levels applied through ammonium sulphate. Jeyaraman and Purushothaman (1988) reported that the application of 10 t/ha of *L. leucocephala* loppings gave an NFE of 50 kg N/ha. Laolao *et al.* (1978)

reported that incorporating 120 kg N/ha as *L. leucocephala* herbage was as effective as a similar amount of ammonium sulphate-N for rice.

The amount of N accumulated by different green manures in different situations may not be sufficient to meet the N-requirements of high-yielding rice cultivars, and fertilizer-N addition may be necessary to achieve the yield potential. Table 37 shows rice grain-yield response to fertilizer-N, and combined use of green manure and fertilizer-N. In various studies, N- substitution with green manuring to obtain comparable grain yield ranged from 30 to 90 kg N/ha, which corresponds to 33 to 75 percent of the fertilizer application alone. It is pointed out that, as with fertilizer-N, application of green-manure N in excess of that needed for optimum rice yields could result in poor efficiency of its use (Bhardwaj 1982; Bhardwaj and Dev 1985; Morris *et al.* 1989; Meelu *et al.* 1992).

The above results indicate a wide range in efficiency of N-transfer from green manure to the rice crop. This is not surprising in view of the many factors operating. While it is clear that considerable fertilizer-N substitution is obtainable, specific recommendations on green-manure/crop production practices can only be made after thorough study at field level under each given set of ecoclimatic and soil conditions.

Response to Azolla

Rice grain yield: Worldwide studies during the last 20 years — as summarized in Table 38 — show substantial yield increases in rice from applying azolla as a basal green manure, as an intercrop in rice or both. The grain yield increases with azolla as a basal manure ranged from approximately 9 to 123 percent but were generally between 25 and 40 percent. Rice grain-yield increases with azolla as a intercrop ranged from 5 to 52 percent. The yield increases depended upon quantity and N-content of azolla, the method of application and soil fertility (Singh 1977a; Rains and Talley 1979; Roy *et al.* 1988). Response to azolla was better in the dry season than in the wet season (Singh 1977a; Pande 1978). Lumpkin (1987) reported that increases in dry-season rice yields with azolla ranged from 5 to 69 percent in studies from Brazil, India, Pakistan and Thailand, as originally reported by Mandal and Bharati (1983), Barthakur and Talukdar (1983), Kannaiyan *et al.* (1983), Subudhi and Singh (1983), Haq and Rosh (1984) and Fiore (1984). In reports from Burma, India, Sri Lanka and Thailand, wet-season rice-yield increases ranged from -1 to 56 percent.

Li (1984) reported from China that whether azolla was used as an intercrop or as a basal manure, its effect on rice yield was the same. Combined application of azolla as basal plus intercrop resulted in further increase in rice yield.

Recovery of N from azolla: Based on N-balance studies, App *et al.* (1980) concluded that transfer to rice of N from azolla incorporated into the soil was quite rapid. The apparent recovery ranged from 24.6 to 39.7 percent (Tsai *et al.* (1962). Soil properties affect the efficiency of azolla as a green manure for rice. In a pot experiment using ^{15}N-labelled azolla, Li (1984) reported that N-recovery rate in the first crop was 20.4 percent. The residual effect in the second crop was 4.3 percent for buckwheat and 5.3 percent for late rice.

N-fertilizer equivalence: Singh (1982) reported that azolla incorporated as a basal plus intercrop produced a grain yield comparable with that from 60 kg N/ha. From China, Su (1983) reported that incorporating azolla at the rate of 40 t/ha (fresh weight) before

TABLE 38
Effect of Azolla green manure on rice grain yield

Green matter t/ha (N addition kg/ha)	Particulars	Rice yield (t/ha)		Reference
		-Azolla	+Azolla	
India				
10 (20-25)	Dry season (basal)	4.7	5.9	Singh (1977a)
5	Wet season (basal)	2.3	2.5	(Singh (1977b)
10			2.8	
15			3.0	
30 (56)	Dry season (2 intercrops)	2.7	4.1	Singh & Singh (1989)
46 (80)	Dry season (basal + 2 intercrops)		4.9	
10	Wet season (basal)	3.9	4.6	Pande (1978)
10	Dry season (basal)	3.3	4.6	
10	Wet season (intercrop)	3.9	4.6	
5	Wet season mean of 5 experiments (basal)	2.8	3.3	Patel *et al.* (1980)
10			3.7	
5	Wet season mean of 5 zones comprising 13 experiments (basal)	3.0	3.3	Pillai *et al.* (1980)
	(intercrop)		3.4	
10	Wet season (basal)	1.9	3.2	Patro *et al.* (1987)
10	Dry season (basal)	1.8	3.1	
(100)	(basal)	2.6	5.1	Rabindra *et al.* (1989)
China				
	Main season (basal)	2.3	3.5-4.0	Ku-Jung Shen (1978b)
21	(intercrop)	3.7	5.0	Liu (1979)
Full cover	Early season (intercrop): mean of 3 azolla species	4.8	5.1	Li (1984)
	(basal + intercrop)		5.9	
USA				
(40)	(basal)	1.3	2.9	Rains & Talley (1979)
	(intercrop)		1.6	
(38)	(basal + intercrop)	1.3	2.1	Talley *et al.* (1977)
Cameroon	Dry season (basal)	6.5	7.2	Roy *et al.* (1988)
	(intercrop)		6.8	
Sri Lanka	(basal)	2.3	2.7	Weerakoon (1983)
Madagascar 10	(basal)	5.8	7.4	Rakotonaisa *et al.* (1988)
Viet Nam	Mean of 5 experiments (basal)	2.6	2.9	Mishustin & Shilnikova (1971)

transplanting rice was equivalent to applying 60 kg N/ha from ammonium sulphate. When an additional 20 t/ha of azolla were incorporated at the mid-tillering stage, the yield effect was equal to 70 kg N/ha from ammonium sulphate.

In India, application of 5 and 10 t/ha of azolla gave rice yields comparable with 30 and 60 kg urea N/ha, respectively (Patel *et al.* 1980). Singh *et al.* (1981b) found that one crop of azolla increased yield and N-uptake of rice as much as did 25-30 kg N/ha applied as urea. Applying two or three crops of azolla increased the yield and N-uptake as much as 60-90 kg N/ha applied as urea. Azolla incorporated as a basal plus intercropped dressing increased rice yield to the same extent as 60 kg N/ha (Singh 1982). Rabindra *et al.* (1989) reported that application of 100 kg azolla N/ha gave a rice-grain yield comparable with that from 100 kg urea N/ha applied in three equal splits.

In Nepal, Joshy (1983) found that azolla could replace 30 kg N/ha by a single incorporation. In Sri Lanka, Weerakoon (1983) reported that incorporation of azolla 14 days before transplanting gave a rice yield comparable with 50 kg N/ha. When azolla was incorporated twice during a single rice-crop cycle, it resulted in grain yield equivalent to applying 69-100 kg of urea N/ha on fallow plots.

In California, the separate effects of azolla and ammonium sulphate on rice yields were similar at the relatively low rate of 40 kg N/ha, with a yield increase of 1.2 t/ha (Talley and Rains 1980b). At a high rate (93 kg azolla N/ha), however, the yield response (2.6 t/ha) was only 70 percent of the response to an equal rate of ammonium sulphate (Talley and Rains 1980a). Watanabe *et al.* (1981) confirmed that the efficiency of N-uptake from azolla was comparable with that from inorganic N.

The above-quoted results show that azolla is an efficient producer and carrier of N to a wetland rice crop, and is capable of contributing N to the same extent as urea up to 100 kg/ha. This is an important finding in terms of cost-effectiveness. Much depends, however, on the practicality of extending its use to large areas of crop production.

MAIZE

Maize crop is grown from the tropics to sub-temperate zones, offers greater scope for both cultural practices and range of green-manure species than applies for wetland rice.

Green Manure in the Rotation

Tropical regions: In the Philippines, Gonzales (1962) reported that mungbean green manure plus 30 kg N/ha produced grain yields of dry-season maize comparable with those from 60 kg N/ha applied on fallow plots. Similar results were obtained in the wet season in a low-rainfall year, but the yields were adversely affected in high-rainfall years. Olan *et al.* (1958) compared the effects of ten green-manure crops on maize. The mean grain-yield response was 0.3 t/ha, 60 percent greater than fallow treatment (although overall yields were low). Among different green manures, *Mucuna pruriens*, *Canavalia ensiformis* and *Crotalaria usaramoensis* produced the maximum biomass and maize yield. Ogbonna and Mabbayad (1983) reported that ploughing-under 90-day-old stylo green manure produced 1.7 t/ha more grain yield of dry-season maize than the control treatment. Application of 30 kg N/ha as green manure

TABLE 39
Response of maize to green manuring

Green manure	Dry biomass (N added kg/ha)	Fertilizer N (kg/ha)	Grain yield (t/ha)		% increase	Reference
			-GM	+GM		
Cowpea	3.8 t/ha	50	2.9	3.3	14	Singh *et al.*
Clusterbean/ sesbania	(91 kg/ha)	125	3.4	4.1	21	(1982)
Cowpea	10 t/ha (F)	0	1.1	1.8	64	Singh & Brar
	(60 kg/ha)	60	2.0	3.0	50	(1985)
		120	2.7	3.5	30	
	20 t/ha (F)	0	1.1	2.8	155	
	(120 kg/ha)	180	3.4	4.1	21	
Ten legumes	-		0.5	0.8	60	Olan *et al.* (1958)
Mungbean	9 t/ha (dry season)	0	1.3	1.8	38	Gonzales (1962)
	13.1 t/ha (wet season)	0	0.7	1.0	43	

F = fresh weight

TABLE 40
Effect of green manuring on grain yield of dry season maize in Latin America

Green manure species	Total N added (kg/ha)	Maize yield (t/ha)		Increase in yield (%)	Reference
		-GM	+GM		
Mucuna aterrima	252	4.9	5.6	14	Bowen (1987)
Mucuna aterrima	117	3.7	6.3	70	Quintana (1987)
Zorina latifolia	58		4.7	27	
Canavalia ensiformes	156		6.1	65	
Crotalaria striata	170		5.8	57	
Canavalia brasiliensis	228	3.3	6.6	100	Carsky (1989)
Cajanas cajan	229		7.0	112	
Canavalia ensiformes	231		6.4	94	
Calopogonium mucunoides	142		6.1	85	
Crotalaria striata	306		6.6	100	
Mucuna aterrima	152		6.3	91	
Pueraria phaseoloides	116		5.7	73	

produced maize yields comparable with that from 90 kg N/ha on fallow plots, indicating a substitution value of 60 kg N/ha from green manuring. In a recent field study, Manguiat *et al.* (1989) observed that grain yield of maize was increased by 80% with stem inoculated *S. rostrata* green manure over control. Green manuring produced similar grain yield of maize as obtained with 45 kg fertilizer N/ha on control plots.

Singh *et al.* (1982) studied the effect of green-manure crops in a maize/wheat rotation. Sesbania, cowpea and clusterbean were sown in the first week of May after the wheat harvest, and were incorporated as 49-day-old crops about 7 days before sowing maize. They found that green manuring in the presence of 50 kg N/ha produced as much maize grain yield as that obtained by applying 125 kg N/ha to the fallow plots, giving a saving of 75 kg N/ha from green manuring (Table 39). Among the green manures tested, cowpea and clusterbean gave better performances than sesbania. Singh and Brar (1985) reported that cowpea green manure at 10 t/ha and 20 t/ha, supplying 60 kg N/ha and 120 kg N/ha, increased maize grain yield by 0.7 (64 percent) and 1.7 t/ha (155 percent) over the control, respectively. Green manure N proved as efficient as fertilizer N for increasing maize grain yield.

Reddy *et al.* (1986) evaluated several tropical legumes as green manures for maize in the United States. Results showed that dry-matter yield of maize on green-manured plots ranged from 3.4 to 5.7 t/ha with a mean of 4.2 t/ha, compared with 2.7 t/ha produced on a fallow plot.

Weerakoon (1983) evaluated fast-growing perennial tropical legumes as cover crops in maize. He noted that maize grown with *Macroptilium atropurpureum* proved the most efficient in increasing maize yield — by 147 percent over the control (no-cover) treatment.

In Brazil, green manuring with different legumes increased maize yield by 0.7 to 3.7 t/ha over control (Table 40). Maize yields up to 6.3 t/ha were achieved using the legume green manure mucuna as the only N source. Smyth *et al.* (1991) calculated mean fertilizer N substitution value of 75 kg N/ha for mucuna green manure and 26 kg N/ha for Indigofera and cowpea residue applied to maize.

Sub-temperate regions: Winter-legume cover crops are particularly desirable where no-tillage maize (or grain sorghum) is grown in southeast United States, where they supplement N input, help to control soil erosion, provide moisture-conserving mulch, and above all are very effective in increasing maize yields (Smith *et al.* 1987).

Several research workers have reported that legume cover crops markedly increase grain yield of following maize, even in the absence of applied N. The grain-yield response of maize to legume cover ranged from 0.4 to 4.4 t/ha in different studies (Table 41). The NFE of winter-legume cover crops as estimated by an indirect method ranged approximately from 50 to 112 kg N/ha. However, Worsham (1986) reported an NFE of 200 kg/ha. These data when compared with total N additions through the legumes suggest that legume residue is a less efficient N source than inorganic fertilizer. In an earlier study by Stickler *et al.* (1959) it was calculated that legume N was generally 25-50 percent as effective as inorganic N. Varco (1986) reported that with no-tillage compared with conventional-tillage management, approximately 20 and 32 percent of the labelled N from the legume was recovered in maize grain plus stover, respectively.

The selected reports quoted above indicate very definite responses of maize to green manuring, but there is conflict of consensus on its efficiency in differing climates - values from tropical conditions exceeding by 100 percent those from sub-temperate areas. The interactions between the variable factors such as green-manure and maize varieties, fertilizer carrier and climatic parameters need more critical analysis.

TABLE 41

Effect of wintr-legume cover crop on maize grain yield and nitrogen fertilizer equivalence of legume green manure

Cover crop	N addition (kg/ha)	Maize yield (t/ha)		N fertilizer equival. (kg/ha)	Reference
		-legume	+legume		
Hairy vetch + rye	158	4.7	9.1	56-112	Mitchell & Teel
Crimson clover + rye	147	4.7	7.5		(1977) (unirrig. crop)
Hairy vetch	209	3.8	6.4	100	Ebelhar *et al.* (1984)
Crimson clover/ big-flower vetch	50-60	3.8	4.3	<50	
Crimson clover		3.8	4.4		Frye *et al.* (1985)
Hairy vetch		3.8	4.2		
Harity vetch	161	5.5	8.2		Wagger (1989)
Crimson clover	126	5.5	7.3		
Crimson clover/peas	229/182	3.0	6.5	<90	Holderbaun *et al.* (1990)

TABLE 42

Effect of alley-cropping with *Leucaena* on grain yield of maize (Kang *et al.* 1985)

Treatment (*Leucaena* prunings and N application)	Maize grain yield (t/ha)				
	1980	1981*	1982	1983	Mean
Removed-No N	1.04	0.48	0.61	0.26	0.60
Retained-No N	1.91	1.21	2.10	1.92	1.79
Retained-80 kg N/ha	3.26	1.89	2.91	3.16	2.81
LSD (P=0.05)	0.31	0.29	0.44	0.79	-

* Maize crop seriously affected by drought

Interplanting with Green Manure

In maize, large inter-row spaces are available which may be more efficiently used for interplanting with a green manure, and thereby possibly replacing part of the fertilizer-N requirement. Chandanani (1958) studied interplanting maize with sunn hemp and clusterbean. The green-manure crop was grown in alternate rows and incorporated 7-8 weeks after sowing. He found that the grain yield was 12 percent less when interplanted with green manure than when in pure stand. The yield of a following wheat crop, however, was 26 percent higher after maize interplanted with green manure.

Agboola and Fayemi (1972) found that interplanting maize with green gram (*Phaseolus aureus*), cowpea and *Calopogonium mucunoides* increased its mean grain yield by 0.5 t/ha over the control. Gueverra (1976) reported that maize interplanted with leucaena gave 23 percent more yield than the control, but efficiency of leucaena-N compared with urea-N was only 38 percent. In the Philippines, Lales (1983) reported that interplanting sunn hemp in combination with 45 kg N/ha produced as much maize yield as that obtained with the application of 90 kg N/ha with no green manure. Pandey and Pendleton (1986) studied the interplanting of soybean as a mixed green manure/bean crop in maize. The soybean/green-manure component increased the mean grain yield of maize by 0.6 t/ha, and the NFE of the green manure was calculated as 28 kg N/ha.

Again a conflicting picture emerges; on the whole it would appear that incorporating a green manure at a stage when it would be capable of contributing a reasonable amount of N would be liable to damage the lateral rooting of the maize, to have too little time to mineralize and in any event to supply the nutrient at a wrong time in the crop's development. The practice is most likely to be of value in a following phase of a rotation.

Green-leaf Manuring

Siagian and Mabbayad (1980) reported that grain yield of maize from treatments receiving 150 kg N/ha through leucaena leaves was comparable with treatments receiving 150 kg N/ha from urea. Herrera (1980) also observed that maize-grain yield increases from applications of leucaena leaves at 90 kg N/ha were comparable with those obtained from an equal quantity of inorganic N supplied as ammonium sulphate. Brewbaker (1985) reported that maize responded linearly to leucaena green-leaf manuring with 24 kg grain/kg N from incorporated leaves, and 14.8 kg grain/kg N from leaves used as mulch.

Kang *et al*. (1985) showed that application of leucaena prunings adding 5.9 to 7.1 t dry matter/ha/year and 173 to 208 kg N/ha per year, increased average maize yields over a 4-year period by 1.19 t/ha (200 percent) over the control (at low yield levels). With no N and no leucaena prunings, maize yields continued to decline drastically (Table 42). In long-term alley-cropping experiments on sandy soils and on degraded alfisols at Ibadan, Nigeria, maize yields, as shown in Figure 14, were significantly higher when cropped with leucaena and gliricidia than in control plots (Kang and Wilson 1987).

The results obtained by Mercado *et al*. (1989) in the Philippines suggest that N contribution from the hedgerows to the alley may be adequate to provide the crop requirement of rice or maize with a 2.5-3.5 t/ha yield target.

In Hawaii, Rosecrance and Kuo (1989) obtained maize yield of 2.2 t/ha in plots alley cropped with *S. sesban* as compared to 0.46 t/ha in the control plots (sole maize crop). A strong relationship was observed between the amount of green leaf manure applied by nine legume trees and maize grain yield. In Costa Rica, significant response to alley farming with gliricidia was observed when bean yield in the control plots was less than 0.8 t/ha and maize yields were less than 1.2 t/ha (Glover 1989).

These results illustrate the potential of green-leaf manuring for at least maintaining maize yields on poor soil that is inherently in need of organic matter.

SORGHUM

In the Philippines, Quillang (1981) observed that incorporating 75 kg N/ha from leucaena leaves 10 days before sowing produced sorghum grain yields comparable with 75 kg N/ha applied as ammonium sulphate. Lower yields were obtained when leucaena leaves were dug-in 20 or 30 days before sowing. San Pascual (1982) reported a yield increase from 2.6

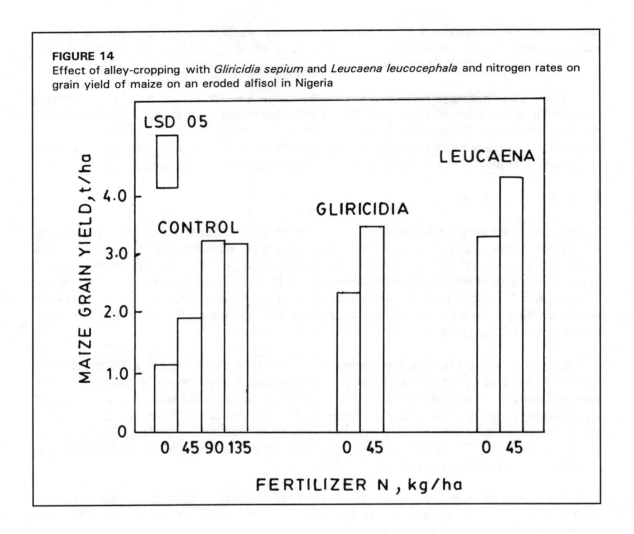

FIGURE 14
Effect of alley-cropping with *Gliricidia sepium* and *Leucaena leucocephala* and nitrogen rates on grain yield of maize on an eroded alfisol in Nigeria

TABLE 43
Effect of green manuring on grain yield of wheat in India

Green-manure crop	Age/biomass	Wheat yield (t/ha)		Reference
		-GM	+GM	
Sunn hemp	56 days	1.6	2.1	Khan & Mathur (1957)
Sunn hemp	49-56 days	2.0	2.3	Chandanani (1958)
Different green-leaf manures	18.4 t/ha (fresh weight)	0.3	1.0	Singh & Sinha (1964)
Sunn hemp/Sesbania	5.6 t/ha (freshweight)			Panse *et al.* (1965)
	mean of 190 expts[1]	1.1	1.3	
	mean of 46 expts[2]	0.6	0.7	
Sunn hemp/Sesbania	-	0.5	0.6	Darra *et al.* (1968)
Sunn hemp	19.3 t/ha	1.6	2.1	Gupta & Gyan Prakash (1969)
Sunn hemp	-	3.1	3.6	Kute & Mann (1969)
Sesbania/Clusterbean	-	1.3	1.6	Chela & Gill (1973)
Sunn hemp	-	1.7	2.5	Verma *et al.* (1990)

[1] Irrigated wheat
[2] Unirrigated wheat

(control) to 3.0 t/ha from green manuring with stylo. The dry-biomass yield of 3.5 t/ha of stylo was equivalent to the application of 60 kg N/ha on fallow plots.

In the semi-arid tropics of India, Singh and Das (1984) observed that grain yield and N uptake of post-rainy-season sorghum were both increased by about 50 percent when manured with leucaena loppings. In the United States, Hargrove (1986) studied the grain-yield response of sorghum to several leguminous winter cover crops. Crimson clover, hairy and common vetch significantly increased the grain yield over fallow by from 0.8 to 1.1 t/ha, and the estimated NFE ranged from 61 to 97 kg N/ha.

WHEAT

In India, before the introduction of high-yielding crop varieties, intensive agriculture and improved irrigation facilities, a rainfed green-manure crop was generally sown after the onset of monsoon rains in July. At about eight weeks of growth the green manure was incorporated into the soil and allowed to decompose before sowing wheat from late October to early November. A compilation of research work on green manuring of wheat given in Table 43 shows that increase in wheat yield with green manuring ranged from 0.1 to 0.8 t/ha. Recently, Nitant (1990) has studied the N contribution from leucaena loppings, and found that application of 50 kg N/ha plus leucaena resulted in higher grain production than that obtained from 150 kg N/ha alone, an NFE of at least 100 kg N/ha.

In the United States, Reddy *et al*. (1986) reported that wheat dry-matter production was significantly higher after tropical legume green manures than after summer fallow. Mahler and Auld (1989) evaluated the green-manuring potential of Austrian winter peas in winter wheat. Incorporating winter peas green manure residue, after harvesting the peas, significantly increased wheat grain yield with an NFE of 94 kg N/ha.

COTTON

Panse *et al*. (1965) summarized previous work on response of irrigated and unirrigated cotton to green-manure crops of sunn hemp or mungbean intercropped and incorporated after 30 days. The results revealed that green manuring of cotton gave little benefit and there was frequently a risk of depression in yield, especially in unirrigated cotton. This was attributed to competition of the green-manure crop for soil moisture and nutrients. However, Mariakulandai and Morachen (1965) reported that green manuring with sunn hemp and sesbania increased the yield of irrigated cotton in India by 16 percent over control, and Rai (1966) noted that green manuring increased seed-cotton yield by 10 percent in Sudan.

In the southern coastal plain of the United States, Touchton *et al*. (1984) in a 2-year trial reported that legume winter cover crops of crimson clover and common vetch, contributing about 100 kg N/ha, increased lint yield of cotton by 0.31 and 0.25 t/ha, respectively, over no-N control (0.59 kg/ha). Cotton yields with legume crops alone were comparable with those obtained from 68 kg fertilizer N/ha on fallow plots.

TABLE 44
Green manuring responses of potato in India

Green-manure crop	Age/N addition	Potato yield (t/ha)		% inc.	References
		-GM	+GM		
Clusterbean/sunn hemp/sesbania	-	16.8	18.0	7	Swaminathan & Singh (1960)
Clusterbean	56 days	13.0	18.6	43	Singh *et al*. (1975)
Sesbania	90 kg N/ha	13.7	18.5	36	Sharma *et al*. (1988)
Sesbania/mungbean	70-90 kg N/ha	9.6	14.7	53	Sharma & Sharma (1988)

TABLE 45
Effect of green manuring and N rates on mean grain yield of raya and toria

Green-manure treatment	Raya (Dhillon *et al*. 1984) kg N/ha			Toria (Pasricha *et al*. 1988) kg N/ha	
	0	100	150	0	60
Without GM	0.46	0.74	0.88	0.22	1.05
With GM	0.76	1.16	1.21	1.05	1.61

POTATO

In rotations that include root crops, green manuring becomes increasingly important as a means of maintaining the organic-matter content of the soil (ten Holte and Van Keulen 1989). Working with potatoes in the Netherlands, they showed that incorporating white clover and red clover at rates of 3.5 t/ha (99 kg N/ha) and 4.7 t/ha (112 kg N/ha) above-ground dry matter gave NFEs of 30 kg and 65 kg N/ha for the two legumes, respectively.

A review by Panse *et al*. (1965) of earlier studies in West Bengal, Bihar and Tamil Nadu (India) on irrigated and unirrigated potato crops revealed large variations in response (-3.2 to +1.5 t/ha) to application of 5.6 t/ha of fresh green manure. The negative responses, which were obtained in West Bengal, may have been due to local conditions inhibiting mineralization of the green manure or possible toxic effects if decomposition occurred under anaerobic conditions. The results of more recent studies in India, as given in Table 44, show that tuber-yield responses of potato to green manuring ranged from 1.2 to 5.6 t/ha. Based on studies over 7 years, Sharma *et al*. (1988) calculated NFEs of 33 and 34 kg N/ha for the sesbania and mungbean green manures, respectively, in the absence of applied N.

OTHER ANNUAL FIELD CROPS

An indicative survey is briefly reported below to illustrate the wide range of environment/annual crop systems under which green manuring has been practised, in addition to those already discussed.

Tobacco: Walunjkar *et al.* (1968) studied the effect of 42-day-old pillipesara (*Phaseolus trilobus*) green manure on tobacco yield. They found that incorporating the tops, equivalent to 40 kg N/ha, gave a cured-leaf yield comparable with that obtained by applying 40 kg fertilizer N/ha. Green manuring also improved leaf quality. Panikar and Sajnani (1975) reported that incorporating 28-day-old sesbania green manure together with farmyard manure at 8 t/ha gave higher total bright-leaf production than FYM alone.

Brassica spp.: Dhillon *et al.* (1984) reported that incorporating clusterbean green-manure tops at 20 t/ha (fresh weight) significantly increased (0.3 t/ha or 65 percent) the grain yield of irrigated raya (*B. juncea*) on a loamy-sand soil. This was equal to the yield produced by applying 100 kg N/ha on no-green-manure plots (Table 45). Pasricha *et al.* (1988) obtained a five-fold increase in grain yield of toria (*B. campestris*) from green manuring with cowpea (Table 45), an NFE of about 60 kg N/ha.

Sugarbeet: In the Netherlands, ten Holte and Van Keulen (1989) reported that incorporating white clover and red clover tops, adding 99-112 kg N/ha, increased sugar yields, by 26 and 31 percent, respectively, over control plots.

Tomato: Deanon (1983) studied the effect of leucaena leaves on tomato yield in the Philippines. The highest yield, 22-24 t/ha, was obtained with the application of 24 t/ha leucaena leaves. This yield was comparable with that produced from the application of inorganic fertilizers at the high rate of 210 kg N + 49.3 kg P + 74.7 kg K/ha. The application of leucaena green leaves also tended to reduce incidence of bacterial blight.

Cabbage: Nastiti (1983) reported marked increases (83-100 percent) in cabbage yield with the incorporation of *Crotalaria usaramoensis* and *Mucuna pruriens*.

Finger millet and castor: Venkateswarlu (1987) reported that green manuring had a beneficial effect on grain yield of dryland crops of finger millet and castor in India.

Cassava: In the Philippines, Castroverde (1983) showed that, when applied at the full recommended rate, stylo green manure produced the same tuber yield of cassava as with the application of urea (equal N basis).

SUGARCANE

Research work on the green-manuring of sugarcane is mostly reported from India. The green-manure crop is either raised before planting the sugarcane or is interplanted with the crop. Results of seventeen experiments conducted in India from 1900 to 1943 showed that the average response of sugarcane to green manuring was 13.6 t cane/ha (Carey and Robinson 1953). Panse *et al.* (1965) reviewing a long-term series of experiments reported that sunn hemp increased cane yield by an average of 18.3 percent, and cowpea by 24.4 percent. Singh (1965) and Srivastava and Pandit (1969) showed that incorporating sunn hemp green manure produced cane yields equal to those obtained with 66-67 kg N/ha applied as ammonium sulphate. Mariakulandai and Morachan (1964) observed that intercropping sugarcane with sunn hemp increased cane yield by 1.7 t/ha over the control. Linge Gowda and Mariakulandai (1972) showed that at a total N of 168 kg/ha, a combination of green-manure N (as intercrop) plus ammonium sulphate produced a cane yield similar to that obtained with ammonium sulphate alone. This suggested that a part of the N requirement of the sugarcane could be met from intercropping with green manure. There was no significant difference in cane yield between green manure incorporated *in situ* or applied as green-leaf manure. In the Philippines, Porquez (1951) reported that a 7-week-old mungbean crop would add about 50 kg N/ha, which was sufficient to meet 50 percent of the N requirement of sugarcane.

RESIDUAL EFFECTS

A full evaluation of a green manure/cropping system should take account of any residual effect operating on a succeeding crop or crops. In view of the transient nature of the expected benefits, such as direct N-contribution, organic matter build-up and improvement of soil physical properties, second-stage residual effects are difficult to quantify or even distinguish other than in terms of yield increase under a given set of cultivation conditions. The following brief review of residual effects — mainly in rice — gives a variable picture from which it is premature to draw hard-and-fast conclusions.

Sethi *et al.* (1952) reviewed green manure research in India and concluded that the residual value of green manure applied to rice was low. Dargan *et al.* (1982) and Bhardwaj and Dev (1985) found no residual effects from sesbania green manure incorporated before rice in a rice-wheat rotation. In a study in which green-manure N levels averaged 85 kg/ha, Morris *et al.* (1986a) did not detect residual-N effects after four years. Panse *et al.* (1965) studied the residual effect of green manure applied to rice on a following rice crop in Andhra Pradesh, Orissa, Uttar Pradesh and West Bengal. There was no residual effect of green manuring in West Bengal, but there were positive effects ranging from 141 kg to 221 kg rice/ha in other States. Furthermore, in Delhi, the residual effect of sunn hemp green manure applied to wheat on a following wheat crop was 211 kg wheat/ha. Tiwari *et al.* (1980) and Sharma and Mittra (1988) reported residual effects of 1.12 and 0.34 t/ha, respectively, from green manure on rice in the succeeding wheat crop. Meelu *et al.* (1992) obtained no significant residual effect in the first year of a two-year evaluation of eight green manure crops, but in the second year, sesbania, the most productive species, gave a significant increase of 0.52 t/ha grain yield for a succeeding dry-season rice crop. Morris *et al.* (1989) also reported a significant residual effect of 0.6 t/ha on a second rice crop from sesbania incorporation adding an average of 123 kg N/ha. Furoc and Morris (1989) found that the mean apparent recovery of N by a dry-season rice crop, estimated by regression analysis, was only 5-6 percent of that in the green manure applied to the wet-season crop. In Latin America, several green manures applied to dry season maize showed marked residual effect ranging from 0.5 to 2.7 t/ha on the grain yield of following wet season maize crop (Lathwell 1990).

In China, the residual effect of milk vetch applied to early rice on the late-rice grain yield was only 0.1 t/ha (Jiao *et al.* 1986). In the United States, Westcott and Mikkelsen (1988) reported that residual values for green manure-N have not been measured in the field, but may contribute from 2 to 9 percent of N applied to the subsequent crops. Frye *et al.* (1985) found an increasing benefit of hairy vetch on maize yield with time, particularly at low rates of added N. Singh *et al.* (1982) studied the residual effect of green manuring of maize on the succeeding wheat crop over three years and obtained an average increase of 0.28 t/ha grain over no green-manure treatment. Bouldin (1988) reported that continued use of green manure over 10 or more years could have considerable residual effect.

Insofar as tuber crops are concerned, the effect of green manure may not be restricted to the first crop after incorporation. Singh *et al.* (1975) observed that tuber yield of spring potato was 3.8 t/ha higher on plots where green manure was applied to the preceding autumn crop than on fallow plots. Sharma and Sharma (1988) observed a significant residual effect of green manure applied to potato in the following wheat crop. Green manuring increased wheat grain yield by 0.2 t/ha over the control. ten Holte and Van Keulen (1989) observed a significant residual effect on the wheat crop of green manuring in preceding sugarbeet and potatoes, the effect being greater after red clover than after white clover.

The above results indicate a need for more critical research into possible residual effects, particularly after long-term use of green manures in rice, and in dryland and tuberous crops where the build-up of soil fertility is important.

Chapter 8

Conclusions

The value of green manuring for maintaining and increasing the productivity of a wide range of soils under various climatic and cropping systems, for reducing erosion losses and for ameliorating the salt-affected soils, has been recognized in a traditional way for a long time, and is supported by the considerable amount of quantitative data adduced in this Bulletin. Nevertheless, in spite of the knowledge and awareness of the practice by research and extension workers and farmers themselves, it has not extended in recent years. In fact, according to Smith *et al.* (1987), recommendations for further research made by authors in 1981 were markedly similar to those made fifty years previously. The apparent ignoring of the practice during that period may have coincided with the increasing availability of mineral fertilizer N such as ammonium sulphate and urea. With their increasing cost, however, and the current trend towards a 'green' approach to agricultural production voicing concern for polluting the environment and avoiding unnecessarily high inputs of non-renewable energy used in the production of fertilizers, the time may well be right for a comprehensive re-assessment of green manuring along certain more promising lines touched on in this Bulletin. Before making specific recommendations, however, it is necessary to bear in mind a number of major constraints operating at farm level to the wider adoption of green manuring.

CONSTRAINTS

The following listing is neither exhaustive as far as all possible conditions are concerned nor in order of priority, although the attempt is made to emphasize economic considerations as pre-eminent:

◻ no obvious or immediate return in cash or kind, except for dual-purpose cropping, and hence labour input considered unproductive;

◻ cost-effectiveness unattractive compared with fertilizer, particularly when high-yielding varieties of rice are grown;

◻ practical difficulty of thorough incorporation;

◻ difficulty and/or cost of seed supply;

◻ control of the quantity and timing of nutrients applied more complex than with fertilizers;

◻   a risk-prone and low-priority crop where soil moisture and water supply are not dependable;

◻   when intercropped, possible competition for soil moisture, nutrients and space with main crop;

◻   when grown on rice bunds may reduce crop yield by shading and root competition;

◻   residual effects not always obvious, particularly in the short-term;

◻   may attract build-up of soil and/or air-borne pests and diseases;

◻   low emphasis on organic manures by research and extension workers, particularly where demonstrations on farmers' fields are concerned.

Although many of the above constraints are inherent to the practice of green manuring, a number of areas are considered to be open for further study.

DEVELOPMENT AND RESEARCH NEEDS

For any realistic approach to be made to extending the use of green manures, it is essential for the extension worker (or equivalent promotion regime) to be armed with factual information derived from critical experiments on farmers' fields as to its economic value in a given cropping ecosystem; in addition, certain lines of immediately practical and more theoretical, basic study are required.

Research/extension

•   evaluation over a four- to five-year period of all socio-economic factors involved using the current state of technology on a typical pilot farmer's field (or equivalent area on a research station to maximize supervision);

•   transfer of evaluation findings to selected farmers over a wider area;

•   general incorporation of successful results into area extension policy;

•   depending on national requirements, it may first be necessary to embark on a coordinated programme of national or even international research, in which input/output parameters would be standardized and environments precisely described, in order to obtain valid analytical comparison for extrapolation of the results.

Practical studies

•   the economic studies outlined above apply to normal and marginally-affected soils, but there remains an increasing need for complementary studies on the reclamation of seriously salt-affected soils, particularly in irrigation areas with imperfect drainage systems;

- definitive determination of optimum age of green-manure crop, depth of incorporation and decomposition time before establishing main crop;

- simple yet effective methods of establishing, and of incorporating green-manure crops at farm level;

- development of systems for increasing productivity of a green-manure crop both for *in situ* and transported green-leaf utilization;

- maximizing unit-area production by means of inter-, mixed- and bund-cropping under various regimes of rainfall and water supply;

- programmes covering the production, storage and distribution at national and farm level, to ensure timely supply, of good quality green-manure seed of high germinability;

- selection of green manure species and genotypes resistant to pests and diseases;

- control measures for green manure pests and diseases where they are of economic importance;

- breeding and selection of superior N_2-fixing species for existing farming lands and also for unfavourable conditions such as uncultivated land, forested and hilly areas;

- extended use of azolla, selection and breeding of improved strains and mineral nutrition to increase its N_2-fixing properties;

- development of simple, on-farm inoculation methods to ensure effective nodulation of leguminous green manures;

- feasibility of vegetative propagation of *S. rostrata*, and simple methods of scarifying the seed at farm level;

- mineral nutrition of green manures, particularly P and minor elements where these may be present at limiting levels.

Theoretical studies

- microbial and chemical kinetics of decomposition products from incorporation of green manures, in relation to crop-plant growth in different soils and moisture regimes;

- dynamics of nutrient release in relation to N-nutrition of the main crop;

- medium-term residual effects of green manuring on soil chemical and physical properties;

- photoperiodic responses of green-manure species to optimize production of non-woody biomass.

The items listed above are neither exhaustive nor in order of priority, but are presented as a working basis for developing an investigation programme.

References

Abrol I.P. 1982. Reclamation of waste lands and world food prospects. Whither Soil Res. pp. 317-337. 12th Int. Congr. Soil Sci., New Delhi, India. 6-18 Feb. 1982.

Abrol I.P. and Bhumbla D.R. 1971. Start with dhaincha on saline-sodic soil. Indian Fmg 21 : 41-42.

Abrol I.P. and Bhumbla D.R. 1979. Crop response to differential gypsum applications in highly sodic soil and the tolerance of several crops to exchangeable sodium under field conditions. Soil Sci. 127 : 79-85.

Agarwal R.R. 1957. Alkali soils can be reclaimed. Indian Fmg 7(9) : 6-8.

Agarwal R.R., Singh M. and Pal C. 1950. Dhaincha as green manure in Uttar Pradesh. Uttar Pradesh Dept Agric. Bull. 104 : 1-24.

Agboola A.A. 1974. Problems of improving soil fertility by the use of green manuring in tropical farming systems. FAO Soils Bull. 27 : 147-164.

Agboola A.A. and Fayemi A.A. 1972. Effect of soil management on corn yield. Agron. J. 64 : 641-644.

Ahmad I. and Niazi R.N.K. 1977. Interaction of soil salinity and aeration on the performance of jantar (*Sesbania aegyptiaca*) and guar (*Cyamopsis psoralioides*) as green manuring crops. Pakistan J. Sci. 29 : 40-42.

Alazard D. and Becker M. 1987. *Aeschynomene* as green manure for rice. Plant Soil 101 : 141-143.

Alazard D. and Duhoux E. 1987. Diversity of stem nodulation sites in *Aeschynomene* sp. J. Plant Physiol. 132 : 123-125.

Alexander M. 1977. Introduction to Soil Microbiology. 2nd edn, John Wiley and Sons, New York.

Allen O.N. and Allen E.K. 1981. In: The Leguminosae, a Source Book of Characteristics, Uses and Nodulation. The University of Wisconsin Press, Wisconsin, Madison. pp. 604-607.

Allison F.E. 1968. Soil aggregation - some facts and the fallacies as seen by a microbiologist. Soil Sci. 106 : 136-143.

Anant Rao N.K., Agrawal J.P., Pawar K.S. and Yadav N.R. 1957. Phosphate manuring of sunhemp green manure. Indian J. Agron. 1 : 215-219.

Antil R.S., Singh D., Kumar V. and Singh M. 1988. Effect of different preceeding crops on yield and nitrogen uptake by rice. Indian J. Agron. 33 : 380-384.

App A., Bouldin D.R., Dart P.J. and Watanabe I. 1980. Constraints to biological nitrogen fixation in soil of the tropics. In: Priorities for alleviating soil-related constraints to food in the tropics, pp. 317-319. Int. Rice Res. Inst. Los Baños, Philippines.

Arakeri H.R. and Patil S.V. 1957. The why and how of green manuring. Indian Farming. 7(1): 24-26.

Arshad M. and Hussain A. 1984. Growth of *Sesbania sesban* under saline conditions. Nitrogen Fixing Tree Res. Rep. 2 : 17.

Arunin S., Dissataporn C., Anuluxtipan Y. and Nana D. 1988. Potential of sesbania as a green manure in saline rice soils in Thailand. In: Green Manuring in Rice Farming, pp. 83-95. Int. Rice Res. Inst., Los Baños, Philippines.

Arunin S., Rungsaengchan P., Dissataporn C. and Yuwaniyama A. 1982. Effect of periods of plowing *Sesbania aculeata* Poir at different ages on the reclamation of salt-affected soil. (Thai, English summary). Res. Report Dept Land Dev., Bangkok.

Arunin S., Yuwaniyama A., Rungsaengchan P., Suttavas A., Mitthampithak V. and Ragland J. 1987. Effect of upland and lowland saline soils on four species of sesbania, (Thai) Ann. Tech. Rep. Dept. Land Dev., Bangkok.

Aspiras R.B. 1966. Some factors affecting ammonification in flooded soils. M.S. Thesis, University of Philippines, Laguna. 59p.

Atta-Krah A.N. 1990. Alley farming with leucaena : Effect of short grazed fallows on soil fertility and crop yield. Expl Agric. 26 : 1-10.

Atta-Krah A.N., Sumberg J.E. and Keynolds L. 1985. Leguminous fodder trees in the farming system. An overview of research in the humid zone. Programme of ILCA in southwestern Nigeria. Ibadan, Nigeria, ILCA.

Bajpai P.D., Arya Ranjana and Gupta B.R. 1980. Comparative studies on decomposition return of some plant materials in two different soil conditions during winter season. Indian J. Agric. Res. 14 : 91-102.

Ballal D.K., Umale S.R. and Nisal B.V. 1968. A study of after effects of green manure crops on yield and uptake of nutrients by wheat. Indian J. Agron. 13 : 165-169.

Bao X., Ding C. and Yu T. 1983. Stability constants of Mn_2 complexes in soils as determined by a voltametric method. Z. Pfl. Ernähr. Düng. Bodenk. 146 : 285-295.

Bao X., Liu Z. and Yu T. 1978. Studies on oxidation reduction processes in paddy soils. IX. Forms of water soluble ferrous iron. Acta Pedol. Sin. 15 : 174-181. (Chinese, English Summary).

Bao X. and Yu T. 1986. Stability constants of Fe(II) complexes in soil. Acta Pedol. Sin. 23 : 40-43.

Barker R., Herdt R.W. and Rose B. 1985. The rice economy in Asia. Resources for the future, Washington, D.C.

Barthakur H.P. and Talukdar H. 1983. Use of azolla and commercial Fertilizer in Jorhat, India. Int. Rice Res. Newsl. 8(1) : 20.

Becker M. 1990. Potential use of the stem-nodulating legumes *Sesbania rostrata* and *Aeschynomene afraspera* as green manure for lowland rice. PhD Thesis. Justus-Liebig University, Giessen, F.R.G.

Becker M., Alazard D. and Ottow J.C.G. 1986. Mineral nitrogen effect on nodulation and nitrogen fixation of stem nodulating legume *A. afraspera*. Z. Pfl. Ernähr. Düng Bodenk. 149: 485-491.

Becker M. Diekmann K.H., Ladha J.K., DeDatta S.K. and Ottow J.C.G. 1991. Effect of NPK on growth and nitrogen fixation of *Sesbania rostrata* as green manure for lowland rice (*Oryza sativa* L.). Plant Soil 132 : 149-158.

Becker M. Ladha J.K. and Ottow J.C.G. 1990. Growth and N_2 fixation of two stem-nodulating legumes and their effect as green manure on lowland rice. Soil Biol. Biochem. 22 : 1109-1119.

Becker M., Ladha J.K., Watanabe I. and Ottow J.C.G. 1988. Seeding vs vegetative propagation of the stem-nodulating green manure *Sesbania rostrata*. Biol. Fertil. Soils 6 : 279-281.

Becking J.H. 1979. Environmental requirements of *Azolla* for use in tropical rice production. In: Nitrogen and Rice, pp. 345-373. Int. Rice Res. Inst., Los Baños, Philippines.

Benites J.R., McCollum R.E., Aznarau A. 1987. Production potential of corn - peanut intrcrops in the humid tropics. In: Tropsoils Technical Rep. 1986-87 (ed. N. Caudle and C.B. McCants). pp. 54-56. North Carolina State Univ., Raleigh.

Benoit R.E., Willits N.A. and Hanna W.J. 1962. Effect of rye winter cover crop on soil structure. Agron. J. 54 : 419-420.

Beri V. and Meelu O.P. 1981. Substitution of nitrogen through green manure in rice. Indian Fmg 31(5) : 6-7.

Beri V. and Meelu O.P. 1983. Effects of blue-green algae and azolla on rice. In: Recycling organic matter in Asia for fertilizer use, pp. 40-52. Asian Productivity Organization, Tokyo.

Beri V., Meelu O.P. and Khind C.S. 1989a. Biomass production, N accumulation, symbiotic effectiveness and mineralization of green manures in relation to yield of wetland rice. Trop. Agric., Trin. 66 : 11-16.

Beri V., Meelu O.P. and Khind C.S. 1989b. Studies on *Sesbania aculeata* (Pers.) as green manure for N-accumulation and substitution of fertilizer N in wetland rice. Trop. Agric., Trin. 66 : 209-212.

Bhagat R.M., Kanwar B.B., Verma T.S. and Minhas R.S. 1988. Nitrogen economy in lowland rice culture. Oryza 25 : 255-260.

Bhardwaj K.K.R. 1974. Note on the distribution and effectiveness of *Sesbania aculeata* (Poir.) in saline-alkali soils. Indian J. Agric. Sci. 44 : 683-684.

Bhardwaj K.K.R. 1982. Effect of age and decomposition period of dhaincha on the yield of rice. Indian J. Agron. 27 : 284-285.

Bhardwaj K.K.R. and Dev S.P. 1985. Production and decomposition of *Sesbania cannabina* (Retz.) Pers. in relation to its effect on the yield of wetland rice. Trop. Agric., Trin. 62 : 233-236.

Bhardwaj S.P., Prasad S.N. and Singh G. 1981. Economizing nitrogen by green manures in rice-wheat rotation. Indian J. Agric. Sci. 51 : 86-90.

Bhatti H.M., Yasin M. and Rashid M. 1985. Evaluation of *Sesbania* green manuring in rice-wheat rotation. In: proceedings of the International Symposium on N and the Environment (N. Malik, ed.), pp. 275-284. NIAB Faisalabad, Pakistan.

Biederbeck V.O. 1978. Soil organic sulphur and fertility. In: Soil Organic Matter (M. Schnitzer and S.U. Khan eds), pp. 273-310. Elsevier Scientific Pub. New York.

Bijay-Singh, Yadvinder-Singh, Sadana U.S. and Meelu O.P. 1992. Effect of green manure (*Sesbania aculeata*), wheat straw and organic manures on DTPA-extractable Fe, Mn, Zn and Cu in a calcareous sandy loam soil at field capacity and under waterlogged conditions. J. Indian Soc. Soil Sci. 40: 114-118.

Bin J. 1983. Utilization of green manure for raising soil fertility in China. Soil Sci. 135 : 65-69.

Biswas T.K. 1988. Ph.D. Thesis, Indian Agricultural Research Institute, New Delhi, India.

Biswas T.D., Roy M.R. and Sahu B.N. 1970. Effect of different sources of organic manures on the physical properties of the soil growing rice. J. Indian Soc. Soil Sci. 18 : 233-242.

Blair G.J. and Boland O.W. 1978. The release of phosphorus from plant material added to soil. Aust. J. Soil Res. 16 : 101-111.

Bolton Jr. H., Elliot L.F., Papandick R.I. and Bezdieck D.F. 1985. Soil microbial biomass and selected enzyme activities. Effect of fertilizers and cropping practices. Soil Biol. Biochem. 17 : 297-302.

Bouldin D.R. 1988. Effect of green manure on soil organic matter content and nitrogen availability. In: Green manuring in rice farming, pp. 151-163. Int. Rice Res. Inst., Los Baños, Philippines.

Bowen W.T. 1987. Estimating the nitrogen contribution of legumes to succeeding maize on an oxisols in Brazil. PhD Thesis. Cornell Univ., Ithaca, New York.

Bowren K.E. and McNaughton W.N. 1967. The effect of controlled cropping on degraded soils. Can. Dept Agric. Publ. No. 1321, Ottawa.

Brewbaker J.L. 1985. The tropical environment for maize cultivation. In: Breeding strategies for maize production improvement in the topics, (Brandolini A. and Salamini F. eds), pp. 47-77. Food and Agriculture Organization/United Nations and Instituto Agronomico I' Oltremare, Firenze, Italy.

Brewbaker J.L. 1987. Leucaena; a genus of multipurpose trees for tropical forestry. In: Ten years of developments in agroforestry. ICRAF, Nairobi, Kenya.

Brewbaker J. and Hilton E.M. 1979. *Leucaena* versatile tropical legume. In: New Agric. Crops, pp. 207-259. AAAS, Selected Symposia. Westview Press, Boulder, Colorado.

Brown S.M., Whitwell T., Touchton J.T. and Burmeter C.H. 1985. Conservation tillage system for cotton production. Soil Sci. Soc. Am. J. 49 : 1256-1260.

Browning G.M. and Milam F.M. 1944. Effect of different types of organic materials and lime on soil aggregation. Soil Sci. 57 : 91-106.

Camara I. and Diara H. 1986. Evaluation de la valeur agronomique de *Sesbania rostrata* comme source d'azote en riziculture irriguée dans la vallée du fleuve Senégal. Paper presented at the IFS-CRDI-ORSTOM Workshop on Biological Improvement of Soil Fertility, 15-19 March 1986. Dakar.

Carangal V.R., Rebancos E.T., Armada E.C. and Tengco P.L. 1992. Integration of food, forage and green manure production systems. Paper presented at the International Rice Research Conference, 25-29 April 1992, IRRI, Los Baños, The Philippines.

Carey T.M. and Robinson P. 1953. The manuring of sugarcane. Emp. J. Expl Agric. 21 : 99-115.

Carsky R.J. 1989. Estimating availability of nitrogen from green manure to subsequent maize crops using buried bag technique. PhD Thesis. Cornell Univ., Ithaca, New York.

Castroverde Y.L. 1983. Cassava production: Influence of tillage, weed control systems, fertilizer sources and harvest age. Ph.D. Thesis, Univerity of Philippines, Los Baños, Philippines.

Chahal D.S. and Khera S.S. 1988. Effect of green manuring on iron transformations in soils under submerged and unsubmerged conditions. J. Indian Soc. Soil Sci. 36 : 433-438.

Chandanani J.J. 1958. Studies on the value and economics of green manuring. Indian J. Agron. 2 : 209-213.

Chandra V., Khanduja S.D., Misra P.N., Samiuddin and Kaul K.N. 1961. Preliminary trials on the use of *Argemone mexicana* on alkaline soils. ICAR Seminar on Weed Control and Green Manuring, Bombay.

Chapman A.L. and Myers R.J.K. 1987. Nitrogen contributed by grain legumes to rice grown in rotations on the Cununurra soils of the Ord irrigations area, Western Australia. Aust. J. Expl Agric. 27 : 155-163.

Char W.P. 1983. A revision of the Hawaiian species of *Sesbania* (Leguminosae). M.S. Thesis, Univ. of Hawaii (USA).

Chater M. and Gasser J.K.R. 1970. Effect of green manuring, farmyard manure and straw on the organic matter of soil and available nitrogen. J. Soil Sci. 21 : 127-137.

Chatterjee B.N., Singh K.I., Pal A. and Maiti, S. 1979. Organic manures as substitutes for chemical fertilizers for high-yielding rice varieties. Indian J. Agric. Sci. 49 : 188-192

Chaudhary M.R. and Bajwa M.S. 1979. Effect of gypsum, green manure dhaincha and paddy straw on the physical properties of three saline soils. J. Res. (PAU) 16 : 7-13.

Chela K.S. and Gill S.S. 1973. Green manuring. Punjab Agric. Univ., Ludhiana. 34 p.

Chen L. 1988. Green manure cultivation and use for rice in China. In: Green manure in rice farming, pp. 63-70. Int. Rice Res. Inst., Los Baños, Philippines.

Chester G., Attoe D.J. and Allen O.N. 1957. Soil aggregation in relation to various soil constituents. Soil Sci. Soc. Am. Proc. 21: 272-277.

Crozat Y., Sangchyosawat C. 1985. Evaluation of different green manures on rice yield in Songhla Lake Basin. Songklanadarino J. Sci. Technol. 7 : 391-397.

CSSRI.1979. A decade of research. Central Soil Salinity Research Institute, Karnal, India, p. 186.

Dabney S.M., Breitenbeek G.A., Griffin J.L. and Hoff B.J. 1989. Subterranean clover cover crop to increase rice yield. Agron. J. 81 : 483-487.

Dabney S.M., Taylor R.W. and Nipper A.W. 1984. Evaluation of cover crops for no-till corn silage production in Louisiana. Proc. Seventh Ann. Southeast No-till System Conf., pp. 18-21. Alabama Agric. Expt Station, Auburn Univerity.

Dargan K.S., Chillar R.K. and Bhardwaj K.K.R. 1975. In alkali soils - green manuring for more paddy. Indian Fmg 25(3) : 13-15.

Dargan K.S., Singh O.P. and Gupta I.C. 1982. Forages and green manure crops. In: Crop Production in Salt Affected Soils, p.237. Oxford and IBH Publishing Co., New Delhi.

Darra B.L., Jain S.V. and Uzzaman Q. 1968. The influence of different green manure crops on soil structure and wheat yield. Indian J. Agron. 13 : 162-164.

Deanon J.B.S. 1983. Ipil-ipil *Leucaena leucocephala* Lam de Wit as a promising fertilizer for potato production. B.S. Thesis, University of Philippines, Los Baños, Philippines.

Debnath N.C. and Hajra J.N. 1972. Transformations of organic matter in soil in relation to mineralization of carbon and nutrient availability. J. Indian Soc. Soil Sci. 20 : 95-102.

De Haan S. 1977. Humus, its formation, its relation with the mineral part of the soil, and its significance for soil productivity. In: Soil organic matter studies Vol. II, pp. 21-30. Int. Atomic Energy Agency, Vienna.

Desai A.D., Seshagiri T. and Seetharama Rao V. 1957. Phosphating of the green manure crop. J. Indian Soc. Soil Sci. 5 : 219-222.

Dhawan C.L., Bhatnagar B.B.L. and Ghai P.D. 1958. Role of green manuring in reclamation. I. Proc. Natn. Acad. Sci. India 27(a): 168-175.

Dhawan C.L., Kahlon S.S. and Prakash V. 1961. Reclamation of saline and alkali soils (Field experiments). Madras Agric. J. 48: 422-428.

Dhillon K.S. and Dhillon S.K. 1990. Relative contribution of green manures in sulphur nutrition of toria (*Brassica campestris*) J. Nuclear Agric. Biol. 20:128-133.

Dhillon K.S., Pasricha N.S., Bahl G.S. and Baddesha H.S. 1984. Supplementation of nitrogen through green manuring in raya (*Brassica juncea* L.). In: Nitrogen in soils, crops and fertilizers. Bull. Indian Soc. Soil Sci. 13 : 304-309.

Diack M. 1986. Multiplication de *Sesbania rostrata* et son effect sur la production du riz. Paper presented at the IFS-CRDI -ORSTOM Workshop on Biological Improvement of Soil Fertility. 15-19 March, 1986. Dakar.

Diekmann K.H. and De Datta S.K. 1990. Effect of seeding rate on dry matter production and N accumulation of *Sesbania rostrata*. Int. Rice Res. Newsl. 15(3) : 22-23.

Diekmann K.H., DeDatta S.K. and Ottow J.C.G. 1991. Nitrogen-15 balance in lowland rice involving various soil N fractions as affected by green manure and urea amendment. Plant Soil (in press).

Do Van C., Watanabe I., Zimmerman T., Lumpkin T.A., De Waha Baillonville. T. 1989. Sexual hybridisation amoung *Azolla* species. Can. J. Bot. 67 : 3482-3485.

Dreyfus B.L., Alazard D. and Dommergues Y.R. 1984. New and unusual microrganisms and niches. In: Current Perspectives in Microbial Ecocolgy (M. Klug and C.A. Reddy eds) pp. 161-169. ASM.

Dreyfus B.L. and Dommergues Y.R. 1980. Non-inhibition de la fixation d'azote atmosphérique par l'azote combiné chez une leguminuese à nodule caulinaires, *Sesbania rostrata*. CR. Acad. Sci. Paris D. 291 : 265-272.

Dutt A.K., Pathania U. and Kumar V. 1983. Growth of *Sesbania sesban*. Nitrogen Fixing Tree. Res. Reports 1 : 5-6.

Eastman J.S. 1986. Potential for the use of legume cover crops, reduced tillage and sprinkler irrigations in Louisiana rice production. M.S. Thesis, Louisiana State University, Baton Rouge, Louisiana.

Ebelhar S.A., Frye W.W. and Belvins R.L. 1984. Nitrogen from legume cover crops for no-tillage corn. Agron. J. 76 : 51-55.

Evans D.O. 1990. What is *Sesbania*? Botany taxonomy, plant geography and natural history of the perennials members of the genus. In: Perennial *Sesbania* species in Agroforestry system (B. Macklin and D.O. Evans, eds.). pp. 5-19. Nitrogen Fixing Tree Association Waimanalo, Hawaii, USA.

Evans D.O. and Rotar P.P. 1987a. Sesbania in agriculture. Westview Press, Boulder, Colorado, p. 192.

Evans D.O. and Rotar P.P. 1987b. Productivity of *Sesbania* species. Trop. Agric., Trin. 64 : 193-200.

Evans J., O'Connor G.E., Turner G.L., Coventry D.R., Fettell W., Mahoney J. and Walsgott D.N. 1989. N$_2$ fixation and its value to soil N increase in lupin, field pea and other legumes in south eastern Australia. Aust. J. Agric. Res. 40 : 791-805.

FAO. 1974. Shifting cultivation and soil conservation in Africa. Soils Bulletin 24, FAO, Rome.

Fiore M.F. 1984. c.f. T.A Lumpkin (1987). Collection, maintenance and cultivation of azolla. In: Symbiotic nitrogen fixation technology, pp. 55-94. (G.H. Elkan, ed.). Marcel Dekkar, Inc., New York.

Frankenberger, W.T. Jr. and Abdelmagid H.M. 1985. Kinetic parameters of nitrogen mineralization rates of leguminous crops incorporated into soil. Plant Soil 87 : 257-271.

Frye W.W., Smilk W.G. and Williams R.J. 1985. Economics of winter cover crop as a source of nitrogen for no-till corn. J. Soil Water Conserv. 40 : 246-258.

Fujii K., Kobayashi M. and Takahashi E. 1972. Amines in the mixture of plant residue and sand incubated under aerobic and waterlogged condition. J. Sci. Soil Manure, Japan 43 : 160-164.

Fuller W.H., Nielson D.R. and Miller R.W. 1956. Some factors influencing the utilization of phosphorus from crop residues. Soil Sci. Soc. Am. Proc. 20 : 218-224.

Furoc R.E. and Morris R.A. 1989. Apparent recovery and physiological efficiency of nitrogen in Sesbania incorporated before rice. Agron. J. 81 : 797-802.

Gale P.M. and Gilmour J.T. 1988. Net mineralization of carbon and nitrogen under aerobic and anaerobic conditions. Soil Sci. Soc. Am. J. 52 : 1006-1010.

Gangwar B. and Singh N.T. 1985. Effect of greengram residue and nitrogen on rice yield. J. Andaman Sci. Assoc. 1 : 61-62.

Garrity D.P. and Flinn J.C. 1988. Farm level management systems for green manure crops in Asian rice environments. In: Green manuring in rice farming, pp. 111-129. Int. Rice Res. Inst., Los Baños. Philippines.

Gaul B., Abrol I.P. and Dargan K.S. 1976. Notes on the irrigation needs of Sesbania aculeata Poir. for green manuring during summer. Indian J. Agric. Sci. 46 : 434-436.

Gaur A.C. 1978. Recycling and utilization of organic wastes as fertilizers. In: India/FAO/Norway seminar on the development of the complementary use of mineral fertilizers and organic materials in India, pp. 109-126. Ministry of Agric. and Irrigation. Krishi Bhavan, New Delhi, India.

Germani G., Reversat G. and Luc M. 1983. Effect of *Sesbania rostrata* on *Hirschanniella oryzae* in flooded rice. J. Nematol. 15: 269-271.

Ghai S.K., Rao D.L.N. and Batra L. 1985. Comparative study of the potential of Sesbanias for green manuring. Trop. Agric., Trin. 65 : 52-56.

Ghai S.K., Rao D.L.N. and Batra L. 1988. Nitrogen contribution to wetland rice by green manuring with *Sesbania* spp. in an alkaline soil. Biol. Fert. Soils 6 : 22-25.

Gillet J.B. 1963. Sesbania in Africa (excluding Madagascar) and southern Arabia. Kew Bull. 17 : 91-159.

Gines H.C., Furoc R.E., Meelu O.P., Dizon M.A. and Morris R.A. 1986. Studies on green manuring rice in farmers' fields. Paper presented at the 2nd Annual Scientific meeting of the Federation of Crop Sciences Soc. of Philippines. Benguet State Univ., Baguio City, Philippines.

Glover N. 1989. *Gliricidia* production and use. Nitrogen Fixing Tree Association, Waimanalo, Hawaii, USA. pp. 15-21.

Goel K.N. and Verma D.R. 1970. A study of the efficiency of leaf powder as ameliorating agent for alkali soil. Recent Advances in Crop Production. Proc. U.P. Inst. Agric. Sci., Kanpur, pp. 139-141.

Gonzales T.T. 1962. The effect of mungo as green manure and ammonium sulphate on the production of hybird corn seed. Philipp. J. Agric. 27 : 131-143.

Gopala Rao H.G. 1956. Effects of green manuring on red loamy soils freshly brought under swamp paddy cultivation with particular reference to availability of iron and manganese. J. Indian Soc. Soil Sci. 4 : 225-231.

Gopalaswamy G. and Vidhyasekaran P. 1987. Effects of green leaf manure on soil fertility and rice. Int. Rice Res. Newsl. 12(2) : 41.

Groffman P.M., Herdrix D.F., Han C. and Crossby Jr. D.A. 1987. In: The role of legumes in conservation tillage system, (J.F. Power ed.) pp. 7-8. Soil Conservation Soc. Am.

Groya F.L. and Sheaffer C.C. 1985. Nitrogen from forage legumes: harvest and tillage effects. Agronomy J. 77 : 105-109.

Gu R.S. and Wen Q.X. 1981. Cultivation and application of green manure in paddy fields of China. In: Proceedings of Symposium on Paddy Soil, pp. 207-219. Science Press, Beijing, Springer-Verlag, New York.

Guevarra A.B. 1976. Cited from Moomaw J.C., Plucknett D., Tilo S.N., Mahihum B.S. and Irestone W.C. (1978). Farming system. In: Int. consultation on ipil-ipil research, pp. 140-141. PCARRD and U.S. Nat. Acad. Sci.

Guevarra A.B., Whitney A.S. and Thompson J.R. 1978. Influence of intra row spacing and cutting regimes on the growth and yield of leucaena. Agron. J. 70 : 1033-1037.

Gupta B.N. and Gyan Prakash. 1969. Effect of sowing sunn hemp for fibre and green manuring on various dates on the succeeding rabi crop of wheat. Indian J. Agron. 14 : 224-229.

Gupta R.D., Jha K.K. and Dev S.P. 1983. Effect of fertilizers and organic manures on the microflora and microbiological processes in soils. Indian J. Agric. Sci. 53 : 266-270.

Hageman N.R. and Shrader W.D. 1979. Effects of crop sequence and nitrogen fertilizer levels on soil bulk density. Agron. J. 71: 1005-1008.

Hale J.K., Hartwig N.L. and Hoffman L.D. 1984. Cyanazine losses in runoff from no-tillage corn in living and dead mulches vs. unmulched conventional tillage. J. Environ. Qual. 13: 105-110.

Halepyati A.S. and Sheelavantar M.N. 1991. Effect of proportions of P application to *Sesbania rostrata* and N substitution rates on rice yields. Oryza 28 : 201-203.

Hansen E.H. and Munns D.N. 1985. Screening of *Sesbania* species for NaCl tolerance. Nitrogen Fixing Tree Res. Reports 3 : 60-61.

Haq N and Rosh D. 1984. *Azolla* as a substitute for fertilizer. Int. Rice Res. Newsl. 9(3) : 24.

Hargrove W.L. 1986. Winter legumes as a nitrogen source for no-till grain sorghum. Agron. J. 78 : 70-74.

Hargrove W.L., Langdeb G.W. and Thomas A.W. 1984. Role of legume cover crop in conservation tillage production system. Am. Soc. Agric. Eng. Paper 84-2038.

Hati N. 1987. Effect of combining chemical N and *Sesbania aculeata* in upland rice. Int. Rice Res. Newsl. 12(2) : 44-45.

Hauser S. 1990. Water and nutrient dynamics under alley cropping versus monocropping in the humid - subhumid transition zone. 14th Int. Congr. Soil Sci. 6 : 204-209.

Hernandez C.C., Posadas S.S. and Coloma B.B. 1958. Progress report on green manuring studies. J. Soil Sci. Soc. Phil. 10 : 61-64.

Hernandez C.C., Villanueva I.E. and Magtang M.V. 1957. The value of legumes as green manure. J. Soil Sci. Soc. Phil. 9 : 52-58.

Herrera L.M. 1980. Placement and time of application of ipil-ipil leaves as source of N for maize. Ph.D. Thesis, University of the Philippines, Los Baños, Philippines.

Herrera W.T., Vejpas C., Garrity D.P., Sompasew V. and Thongpan N. 1989. Development of green manure technology for rainfed lowland rice on acid infertile soils in Northeast Thailand. Paper presented at the IRRI Saturday Seminar, April 15, 1989.

Herridge D.F. and Brockwell J. 1988. Contributions of fixed nitrogen and soil nitrate to the N economy of irrigated soybean. Soil Biol. Biochem. 20 : 711-717.

Holderbaum J.F., Decker A.M., Meisinger J.J., Mulford F.R. and Vough L.A. 1990. Fall-seeded legume cover crops for no-tillage corn in the humid east. Agron. J. 83 : 117-124.

Hoyt G.D. and Hargrove W.L. 1986. Legume cover crops for improving crop and soil management in Southern United States. Hort. Sci. 21 : 397-402.

Huang D.M., Gao J.H. and Zhu P.L. 1981. The transformation and distribution of organic and inorganic fertilizer nitrogen in rice -soil system. Acta Pedol. Sin. 18 : 107-121. (Chinese, English summary)

Hundal H.S., Biswas C.R. and Vig A.C. 1987. The utilization by rice of P from different ^{32}P-labelled green manures. Biol. Wastes 22 : 97-105.

Hundal H.S., Biswas C.R. and Vig A.C. 1988. Phosphorus sorption characteristics of flooded soil amended with green manures. Trop. Agric., Trin. 65 : 185-187.

Huxley P.A. 1986. Rationalizing research on hedgerow inter cropping: an overview. ICRAF Working Pap. 40. Int. Council Res. Agroforest., Nairobi, p.148 (Mimeo).

ICRAF. 1987. International Council for Research in Agroforestry. Field station status report, March 1987. Nairobi, p.54 (Mimeo).

IRRI. 1986. Annual Report, 1985. Int. Rice Res. Inst., Los Baños, Philippines.

Ishikawa M. 1963. Soil scientific and plant nutritional study on the milk vetch manuring of rice. Tokyama Agric. Exp. Stn. Spec. Stud. Rep.5.

Ishikawa M. 1988. Green manure in rice - The Japan experience. In: Green manuring in rice farming, pp. 45-61. Int. Rice Res. Inst., Los Baños, Philippines.

Iu K.L., Pulford I.D. and Duncan H.J. 1981. Influence or waterlogging and time of organic matter additions on the distribution of trace metals in an acid soil. Plant Soil 59 : 327-333.

Jauhari S.C. and Verma M.M. 1981. Effects of leaching and ameliorants on reclamation of alkali soils. Vigyan Parishad Anusandhan Patrika 24 : 347-354.

Jen Y.M., Lee K.L. and Wu C.C. 1965. Studies on the plantings of *Sesbania aegyptiaca* and its effect on the amelioration of saline soils of the coastal areas of Pan-Chun, Liaoning Province. Acta Pedol. Sin. 13 : 365-376.

Jeyaraman S. and Purushothaman S. 1988. Leucaena as green leaf manure for lowland rice. Int. Rice Res. Newsl. 13(5) : 27.

Jha K.P., Dinesh Chandra and Nanda B.B. 1980. Yield and N uptake of rice as influenced by green leaf manures with *Ipomoea carnea*. Oryza 17 : 18-23.

Jia Z. 1986. Green manure and soil microorganisms. In: Green manure in China, (Jiao Bin, ed.), pp. 113-120. Publishing House of Agric., Beijing, China.

Jiao B., Gu R. and Zhang X. 1986. Chinese green manure. Publishing House of Agric., Beijing, China.

John P.S., Buresh R.J., Pandey R.K., Prasad R. and Chua T.T. 1989a. N-15 balance for urea and neem-coated urea applied to lowland rice following two cowpea cropping systems. Plant Soil 120 : 233-242.

John P.S., Buresh R.J., Prasad R. and Pandey R.K. 1989b. Nitrogen gas ($N_2 + N_2O$) flux from urea applied to lowland rice as affected by green manure. Plant Soil 119 : 7-13.

John P.S., Pandey R.K., Buresh R.J. and Prasad R. 1989c. Lowland rice response to urea following three cowpea cropping systems. Agron. J. 81 : 853-857.

Joseph P.A. 1986. Dhaincha as an organic source of nutrients for rice. Agric. Res. J. Kerala 24: 80-92.

Joshi R.C., Maokip D.D. and Singh K.N. 1990. Effect of green manuring on the improvement of physical conditions of soil under rice-wheat cropping system. Int. Sym. on Natural Resources Management for a Sustainable Agriculture. pp. 61-62, New Delhi.

Joshy D. 1983. Country reports - Nepal. In: Recycling organic matter in Asia for fertilizer use, pp 155-163. Asian Productivity Organization, Tokyo.

Kabeerathumma S., Ghosh S.P. and Lakshmi K.R. 1985. Soil erosion and surface runoff: multiple systems compared. Cassava Newsl. 9 : 5.

Kaila A. 1954. Microbiological fixation and mineralization of phosphorus during the decomposition of organic matter. Z., Pfl-Ernähr Düng. Bodenk. 64 : 27-35 (c.f. Soil Fertil. 17 : 946).

Kadke J.R. 1965. Hastening decomposition of incorporated green manure. Indian J. Agron. 10 : 443-446.

Kalidurai M. and Kannaiyan S. 1990. Effect of sesbania and azolla on rice grain and straw yields. Int. Rice Res. Newsl. 15(2) : 26.

Kamprath E.J., Chandler W.V. and Krantz B.A. 1958. Winter cover crops: Their effects on corn yields and soil properties. North Carolina Agricultural Exptl Station, Tech. Bull. 129.

Kang B.T., Grimme H. and Lawson T.L. 1985. Alley cropping sequentially cropped maize and cowpea with Leucaena on a sandy soil in Southern Nigeria. Plant Soil 85 : 267-277.

Kang B.T. and Wilson G.F. 1987. The development of alley-cropping as a promising agroforestry technology. In: Agroforestry a decade of development. (H. A. Stepplar and P.K.R. Nair eds), pp. 227-243. ICRAF. Nairobi, Kenya.

Kannaiyan S., Thangaraju M. and Oblisami G. 1983. Effect of *Azolla* green manuring on the rice crop. Sci. Cult. 49(7) : 217-219.

Karuppiah V.K.R. and Thangamuthu G.S. 1986. Study on the efficiency of phosphorus forms in combination with organic manures in lowland rice. In: Rock phosphates in agriculture, pp. 209-212 Tamil Nadu Agric Univ. Coimbatore, India.

Katyal J.C. 1977. Influence of organic matter on the chemical and electrochemical properties of some flooded soils. Soil Biol. Biochem. 9 : 259-266.

Keating B.A. and Fisher M.J. 1985. Comparative tolerance of tropical grain legumes to salinity. Aust. J. Agric. Res. 36 : 373-384.

Khan A.R. and Mathur B.P. 1957. Effect of sunhemp as green manure on the yield of wheat. Indian J. Agric. Sci. 27 : 171-176.

Khind C.S., Garg A. and Bajwa M.S. 1989. Effect of sesbania green manure and wheat straw on ammonia volatilization loss in wetland soil. Int. Rice Res. Newsl. 14(2) : 31-32.

Khind C.S., Josan A.S. and Beri V. 1985. N release from sesbania green manure and effect of time of application of N fertilization on lowland rice. Int. Rice Res. Newsl. 10(4) : 26-27.

Khind C.S., Jugsujinda A., Lindau C.W. and Patrick Jr W.H. 1987a. Effect of sesbania straw in a flooded soil on soil pH, redox potential and water soluble nutrients. Int. Rice. Res. Newsl. 12(3) : 42-43.

Khind C.S., Maskina M.S. and Meelu O.P. 1987b. Effect of time of application of *Sesbania aculeata* green manure and fertilizer nitrogen on yield of wetland rice. J. Indian Soc. Soil Sci. 35 : 143-145.

Kolar J.S. and Grewal H.S. 1988. Green manure to sustain productivity and save nitrogen for rice in a rice-wheat cropping system. Int. Rice Res. Newsl.13(4) : 29.

Krishna Rao P.N.A. 1957. Green manure - the cheaper way to more profit. Indian Fmg. 7(8):9.

Krishna Rao D.V. and Murthy V.M.M.S. 1962. Green manuring of rabi paddy crop in sandy loam soils of Telengana. Andhra Agric. J. 9 : 197-201.

Krishna Rao D.V. and Raja Rao G. 1960. Final report of the scheme for land reclamation. Andhra Pradesh Dept of Agric., Andhra Pradesh, India.

Krishna Rao D.V., Seshagiri Rao T. and Krishnamurthy P. 1961.Green manure as a source of nitrogen to rice grown in regurs of the Nizam Sagar Project area. J. Indian Soc. Soil Sci. 9 : 119-123.

Ku-Jung-Shen. 1978a. Ecological characteristics and cultivation practices of milk vetch (*Astragalus sinicus* L.) In: Proceedings India/FAO/Norway seminar on the development of the complementary use of mineral ferilizers and organic materials in India. pp. 217-221. Ministry of Agric. and Irrigation. Govt of India, Krishi Bhavan, New Delhi.

Ku-Jung-Shen. 1978b. Use of azolla as bio-fertilizer - China's Scene. In: Proceedings India/FAO/Norway seminar on the development of the complementary use of mineral fertilizers and organic materials in India, pp. 237-238. Ministry of Agric. and Irrigation. Govt of India, Krishi Bhavan, New Delhi.

Kulasooriya S.A. and Samarakoon I.M. 1990. Decapitating young *Sesbania rostrata* plants to increase biomass production and nitrogen fixation. Int. Rice Res. Newsl. 15(2) : 25-26.

Kulkarni K.R. and Pandey R.K. 1988. Annual legumes for food and as green manure in a rice-based cropping system. In: Green manure in rice farming, pp. 289-299. Int. Rice Res. Inst., Los Baños, Philippines.

Kundu D.K., Shinde J.E., Rao K.V. and Gandhi G. 1990. Green manuring for sustainable agriculture. I. N-release pattern and efficiency of two green manures in a submerged vertisol grown to rice. Int. Symp. Natural Resources Management for a Sustainable Agriculture. pp. 60-61.

Kute S.B. and Mann H.S. 1968. Effect of green manuring on physical, chemical and biological properties of the soil. Indian J. Agron. 13 : 20-25.

Kute S.B. and Mann H.S. 1969. Effect of green manuring on the composition of soil and wheat crop and the balance of major plant nutrients in the soil after the crop. Indian J. Agric. Sci. 39 : 10-17.

Ladha J.K., Miyan S. and Garcia M. 1989. *Sesbania rostrata* green manure for lowland rice : growth, nitrogen fixation *Azorhizobium* spp. inoculation and effects on succeeding crop yields and nitrogen balance. Biol. Fert. Soils 7 : 191-197.

Ladha J.K., Pareek R.P. and Becker M. 1992. Stem-nodulating legume-Rhizobium symbiosis and its agronomic use in lowland rice. Adv. Soil Sci. 20:147-192.

Ladha J.K., Watanabe I. and Saono S. 1988. Nitrogen fixation by leguminous green manure and practices for its enhancement in tropical lowland rice. In: Green manure in rice farming, pp. 165-183. Int. Rice Res. Inst., Los Baños, Philippines.

Ladha J.K., Garcia M., Miyan S., Padre A.T. and Watanabe I. 1989. Survival of *Azorhizobium caulinodans* in the soil and rhizosphere of wetland rice under *Sesbania rostrata* rice rotation. Appl. Environ. Microbiol. 55 : 454-460.

Lales J.S. 1983. Establishment methods for potential of *Crotalaria juncea* L. as green manure for corn. Ph.D. Thesis, University of Philippines, Los Baños, Laguna.

Laolao M.B., Alferez A.C. and Mabbayad B.B. 1978. Response of flooded and non-flooded rice to ipil-ipil leaves fertilization. Philipp. J. Crop Sci. 3 : 195-199.

Lathwell D.J. 1990. Legume green manuring - principles for management based on recent research. Tropsoils Bull. No. 90-01. North Carolina State University, Raleigh, USA.

Li S. 1984. Azolla in the paddy field of western China. In: Organic matter and rice, pp. 169-172. Int. Rice Res. Inst., Los Baños, Philippines.

Li Z., Zu S., Mao M. and Lumpkin T. 1982. Study on the utilization of eight azolla species in agriculture. I. An investigation of their utilization properties. Chinese Agric. Sci. 1 : 19-27.

Linge Gowda B.K. and Mariakulandai A. 1972. Intercropping green manure versus green leaf manure on sugarcane yeild. Madras Agric. J. 59 : 312-317.

Liu Chung-Chu 1987. Reevaluation of *Azolla* utilization in agricultural production. In: *Azolla* utilization. pp. 67-76. Int. Rice Res. Inst., Los Baños, Philippines.

Liu C. 1988. Integrated use of green manure in rice fields in south China. In: Green manure in rice farming, pp. 319-331. Int. rice Res. Inst., Los Baños, Phillippines.

Liu D. 1981. The cultivation of wild leguminous green manure - <u>Aeschynomene</u> <u>indica</u> L. in summer season. Fujiian Nongyckeji 78 : 42-43.

Liu Z. 1979. Use of azolla in rice production in China. In: Nitrogen and Rice. Int. Rice Res. Inst., Los Baños. Philippines.

Lowendorf H.B. 1982. Biological nitrogen fixation in flooded rice fields. Cornell International Agriculture Mimeograph 96, pp. 76.

Lu Shu-ying, Zhou Zhang-bin and Chen Ke-Zeng 1966. Effects of phosphoric fertilizers on increasing the multiplication of Red Azolla and on the nitrogen fixation. Turang Tongbao 2 : 7-9.

Lumpkin T.A. 1987. Collection, maintenance and cultivation of azolla. In: Symbiotic nitrogen fixation technology, (G.H Elkan, ed.), pp. 55-94. Marcel Dekkar Inc, New York.

Lumpkin T.A. and Bartholomew D.P. 1986. Predictive models for the growth response of eight Azolla accessions to climatic variables. Crop Sci. 26 : 107-111.

Lumpkin T.A. and Plucknett D.L. 1982. Azolla as a green manure: Use and management in crop production. Westview Press, Boulder, Colorado.

MacRae R.J. and Mehyus G.R. 1985. The effect of green manuring on the physical properties of temperate-area soils. Adv. Soil Sci. 3 : 71-94.

Magbanua R.D., Garrity D.. Aggarwal P.K., Samson B.T., Liboon S.P. and Morris R.A. 1991. Management strategies of integrating forage legumes for sustainability in low-input upland rice-based cropping systems. Paper presented at the 7th Annual Scientific Conference of the Federation of Crop Science Societies of the Philippines. Bureau of Soils and Water Management, Diliman, Quezon City, 7-9 October 1991.

Mahalingam P.K. 1973. Ameliorative properties of lignite fly ash in reclaiming saline and alkali soils. Madras Agric. J. 60: 1055-1057.

Mahler R.L. and Auld D.L. 1989. Evaluation of the green manure potential of Austrian winter peas in Northern Idaho. Agron. J. 81: 258-264.

Mandal B.K. and Bharati A.K. 1983. *Azolla pinnata* as an organic manure for rice in West Bengal. Indian J. Agric. Sci. 53 : 472-475.

Manguiat I.J., Guinto D.F., Perez A.S. and Pintor R.M. 1992. Response of rainfed lowland rice to green manuring with *Sesbania rostrata*. Trop. Agric. (Trinidad) 69 : 73-77.

Manguiat I.J., Perez A.S. and Jalalon A.T. 1989. Green manuring of corn with inoculated *Sesbania rostrata*. Philipp. J. Crop Sci. 14 : 15-19.

Mann H.H. 1959. Field studies in green manuring. II. Emp. J. Expl. Agr. 27 : 243-251.

Mann H.H. and Tamhane V.A. 1910. The salt lands of the Nira Valley. Bull. Bombay Dep. Agric. 39 : 35.

Mariakulandai A. and Morachen Y.B. 1964. A review of results of manurial trials on sugarcane in Madras state. Madras Agric. J., 51 : 127-138.

Mariakulandai A. and Morachen Y.B. 1965. Results of manurial trials in Madras state on cotton. Madras Agric. J. 52 : 147-155.

Maskey S.L. and Bhattarai S. 1984. Use of indigenous plant materials as nutrient source for rice. Nepalese J. Agric. 15 : 191-192.

Maskina M.S., Sandhu P.S. and Meelu O.P. 1985. Effect of integrated use of organic and inorganic nitrogen sources on growth and nutrient composition of rice seedlings. Oryza 22 : 11-16.

Mathur O.P., Singh V.S., Bishnoi S.L. and Singh B. 1973. Reclaiming saline-alkali soils in Rajasthan canal command areas. Indian Fmg. 23(2) : 15-17.

Maurya P.R. and Ghosh A.B. 1972. Effect of long-term manuring and rotational cropping on fertility status of alluvial calcareous soil. J. Indian Soc. Soil Sci. 20 : 31-43.

Meelu O.P. and Morris R.A. 1988. Green manure management in rice-based cropping systems. In: Green manure in rice farming, pp. 209-222. Int. Rice Res. Inst., Los Baños, Philippines.

Meelu O.P. and Rekhi R.S. 1981. Mung straw management and nitrogen economy in rice culture. Int. Rice Res. News. 6(4) : 21.

Meelu O.P., Morris R.A., Furoc R.E. and Dizon M.A. 1992. Grain yield responses in rice to eight tropical green manures. Trop. Agric., Trin. 66:133-136.

Meelu O.P. Yadvinder-Singh and Bijay-Singh. 1990. Green manure and crop residue management in wetland rice production. 14th Int. Congr. Soil Sci. 4 : 734-735.

Mendiratta R.S., Darra B.L., Singh H. and Singh Y. 1972. Effect of some cultural, chemical and manurial treatments on the chemical characteristics of saline sodic soils under different crop rotations. Indian J. Agric. Res. 6 : 81-89.

Mercado A.R. Jr., Tumacas A.M. and Garrity D.P. 1989. The establishment and performance of tree legume hedgerows in farmers' fields in a slopping acid upland environment. Paper presented at the 5th Annual Scientific Meeting of the Federation of Crop Science Societies of the Philippines held at Iloilo City, 26-29 April 1989.

Metzner J.K. 1982. Agriculture and population pressure in Sikka Isle of Flores. A contribution to the stability of agricultural systems in the wet and dry tropics. Monograph 28. Australian National University, Canberra, Australia.

Miller D.E. and Kemper W.D. 1962. Water stability of aggregates of two soils as influenced by incorporation of alfalfa. Agron. J. 54 : 494-496.

Mirchandani T.J. and Khan A.R. 1952. Effect of age of sunnhemp on the succeeding wheat crop. Green Manuring. ICAR Review Series 6, p. 37.

Mishustin E.N. and Shil'nikova. 1971. Biological fixation of atmospheric nitrogen. MacMillan, London.

Misra P.N. 1976. Effect of some organic and inorganic soil amendments with and without NPK fertilization on paddy yield on saline-sodic soils. Indian J. Agric. Res. 10 : 253-257.

Mitchell W.H. and Teel M.R. 1977. Winter annual cover crops for no-tillage corn production. Agron. J. 69 : 569-573.

Mo S. and Qian J. 1983. Studies on the transformation of nitrogen of milk vetch in red earth and its availablity to rice plant. Acta Pedol. Sin. 20 : 12-22.

Moong F.A. 1986. In: Forages in South East Asian and South Pacific Agriculture. G.J. Blair, D.A. Ivory and T.r. Evans (eds.). pp. 152-156. ACIAR, Canberra, Australia.

Morachan Y.B., Moldenhauer W.C. and Larson W.E. 1972. Effect of increasing amounts of organic residues on continuous corn. I. Yields and soil physical properties. Agron. J. 64 : 199-203.

Morris R.A., Furoc R.E. and Dizon M.A. 1986a. Rice responses to a short-duration green manuure. I. Grain yield. Agron. J. 78 : 409-412.

Morris R.A., Furoc R.E. and Dizon M.A. 1986b. Rice responses to a short-duration green manure. II. N recovery and utilization. Agron. J. 78 : 413-416.

Morris R.A., Furoc R.E., Rajbhandari N.K., Mongersen E.P. and Dizon M.A. 1989. Rice responses to waterlog-tolerant green manures. Agron. J. 81 : 803-809.

Mortensen J.L. and Young J.L. 1960. Effect of summer-seeded green manures on soil structure and availability of nitrogen. Ohio Agric. Exp. Sta. Res. Bull. No. 865.

Motomura S. 1962. The effect of organic matter on the formation of ferrous iron in soil. Soil Sci. Pl. Nutr. 8 : 20-29.

Mughogho S.K., Awai J., Lowendroff H.S. and Lathwell D.J. 1982. The effects of fertilizer nitrogen and *Rhizobium* inoculation on yield of cowpea and subsequent crops of maize. In: Biological Nitrogen Fixation Technology for Tropical Agriculture. P.H. Graham and S.C.Harris (eds.). pp. 297-301. CIAT, Cali, Colombia.

Mulongoy K. and Sanginga N. 1990. Biological nitrogen fixation in alley farming. 14th Int. Congr. Soil. Sci. 3:326-327.

Nagarajah S. 1988. Transformation of green manure nitrogen in lowland rice soils. In: Green manure in rice farming, pp. 193-208. Int. Rice Res. Inst., Los Baños, Philippines.

Nagarajah S. and Amarasiri S.L. 1977. Use of organic materials as fertilizers for lowland rice in Sri Lanka. In: Soil organic matter studies, pp. 97-104. Vol. II. International Atomic Energy Agency, Vienna.

Nagarajah S., Neue H.U. and Alberta M.C.R. 1989. Effect of sesbania, azolla and rice straw incorporation on the kinetics of NH_4, K, Fe, Mn, Zn and P in some flooded soils. Plant Soil 116 : 37-48.

Nair P.K.R. 1988. Use of perennial legumes in Asian farming systems. In: Green manuring in rice farming , pp. 301-317, Int. Rice Res. Inst., Los Baños, Philippines.

Nastiti S.H. 1983. Country reports. Indonesia. In: Recycling organic matter in Asia for fertilizer use, pp. 119-223. Asian Productivity Organization, Tokyo.

National Academy of Sciences. 1979. Tropical Legumes : Resources for the Future. Washington. p. 331.

Nayyar V.K. and Takkar P.N. 1989. Combating iron deficiency in rice grown in sandy soils of Punjab. Int. Symp: Managing Sandy Soils, pp. 379-384, Central Arid Zone Res. Inst., Jodhpur, India.

Nitant H.C. 1990. Supplementation of nitrogen through green leaf manuring (*Leucaena leucocephala*) in wheat. Int. Symp. on natural resources management for a sustainable agriculture, New Delhi. pp. 221-222.

Obenshain S.S. and Gish P.T. 1941. The effect of green manure crops on certain properties of Berks silt loam. Virginia Exp. Stn. Techn. Bull. 73.

Ogbonna C.K.C. and Mabbayad B.B. 1983. Effects of incorporation of 90-day-old stylo as GM on the yield of corn and soil properties. Philipp. J. Crop Sci. 8 : 129-132.

Olan V.R., Subido P.S. and Aquino D.I. 1958. Comparative study of various green manure crops on crop production. Plant Ind. Dig. 21: 28-32.

O'Sullivan T.E. 1985. Farming systems and soil management : the Philippines/Australian development assistance program experience. In: Soil erosion and development. (E.T. Craswell, J. V., Remenyi and L.G. Nallana eds) ACIAR Proceedings Series 6, Canberra.

Palaniappan S.P. and Srinivasulu D. 1990. Biological nitrogen production potential of *Sesbania rostrata* and its utilization by rice. 14th Int. Congr. Soil Sci. 3 : 323-324.

Palm D., Weerakoon W.L., De Silva M.A.P. and Thomas R. 1988. Nitrogen mineralization of *Sesbania sesban* used as green manure for lowland rice in Sri Lanka. Plant Soil 108 : 201-209.

Pande H.K. 1978. Azolla: A precious organic nitrogen fertilizer for rice. In: Proceedings India/FAO/Norway Seminar, Complementary use of mineral fertilizers and organic materials in India, pp 232-236. Ministry of Agric. and Irrigation. Govt of India. Krishi Bhavan, New Delhi.

Pandey R.K. and Pendleton J.W. 1986. Soybeans as green manure in a maize intercropping system. Expl Agric. 22 : 179-185.

Panikar S.N. and Sajnani B.T. 1975. Effect of manures, fertilizers and topping on Virginia tobacco in north Bengal. Indian J. Agron. 20 : 24-25.

Panse V.G., Abraham T.P. and Leelavathi C.R. 1965. Green manuring of crops (Review of experimental results in India), Indian Council Agr. Res. Tech. Bull. No. 2, p.84.

Pareek R.P., Ladha J.K. and Watanabe I. 1990. Estimating N_2 fixation by *Sesbania rostrata* and *S. cannabina* (Syn. *S. aculeata*) in lowland rice soil by the ^{15}N dilution method. Biol. Fertil. Soils 10:77-88.

Pasricha N.S., Aulakh M.S., Bahl G.S. and Baddesha H.S. 1988. Fertilizer use reseach in oilseed crops. Fert. News 33(9) : 15-22.

Patel C.S., Jai-Singh, Mittra B.N., Patro G.K. and Suhravordy M.Z. 1980. Use of *Azolla* fern as a good source of organic nitrogen in rice. Fert. News 25(6) : 15-17.

Patro G.K., Mohanty K. and Jena B.K. 1987. Efficiency of azolla as an organic N source for rice. Int. Rice Res. Newsl. 12(6) : 34-35.

Peoples M.B. and Herridge D.F. 1990. Nitrogen fixation by legumes in tropical and subtropical agriculture. Adv. Agron. 44:155-223.

Peoples M.B., Herridge D.F. and Bergersen F.J. 1988. Measurement of nitrogen fixation in crop and shrub legumes. In: Green manure in rice farming, pp. 223-237. Int. Rice Res. Inst., Los Baños, Philippines.

Pieters A.J. 1927. Green manuring principles and practices. John Wiley and Sons Inc., New York. pp. 356.

Pillai K.G., Choudhary D.B.B. and Krishnamurthy K. 1980. Bio-fertilizers in rice culture - problems and prospects for large scale adoption. Fert. News 25(2) : 40-45.

Ponnamperuma F.N. 1965. Dynamics aspects of flooded soils and the nutrition of the rice plant. In: Mineral nutrition of the rice plant, pp. 295-328. Johns Hopkins Press, Baltimore, Maryland.

Ponnamperuma F.N. 1972. The chemistry of submerged soils. Adv. Agron. 24: 29-96.

Ponnamperuma F.N. 1976. Temperature and the chemical kinetics of flooded soil. In: Climate and Rice, pp. 249-263. Int. Rice Res. Inst., Los Baños, Philippines.

Ponnamperuma F.N. 1984. Improving rice production during the 1984 wet season. Technology Transfer Workshop. March 15-16, Int. Rice. Res. Inst., Los Baños, Philippines.

Poonia S.R. and Bhumbla D.R. 1972. Effect of ESP on the availability of Ca from soil and added gypsum to maize and dhaincha. Plant Soil 36 : 671-679.

Poonia S.R. and Bhumbla D.R. 1973a. Availability of Ca from $Ca^{45}SO_4$ in a highly saline sodic soil. Plant Soil 38 : 675-678.

Poonia S.R. and Bhumbla D.R. 1973b. Effect of farmyard manure on availability of Ca from $Ca^{45}CO_3$ in a sodic soil. Plant Soil 38 : 679-682.

Poonia S.R. and Bhumbla D.R. 1974. Effect of exchangeable sodium percentage on the availability of Ca from soil and added $^{45}CaCO_3$ to *Zea mays* L. and *Sesbania cannabina* (Retz.) Pers. Indian J. Agric. Sci. 43 : 954-959.

Poonia S.R. and Jhorar L.R. 1974. Effect of different concentrations and ratios of Ca and Na in the growth medium on yield and chemical composition of wheat and dhaincha. Indian J. Agric. Sci. 44 : 871-874.

Porquez P.P. 1951. Mungo as source of nitrogen and organic matter for the cane fields. J. Soil Sci. Soc. Phil. 3 : 207-208.

Poyser E.A., Hedlin R.A. and Ridley A.O. 1957. The effect of farm and green manures on the fertility of blackearth-meadon clay soils. Can. J. Soil Sci. 37 : 48-56.

Prasad R. and Palaniappan S.P. 1987. Pulse crop residue as N source in rice-based cropping system. Int. Rice Res. Newsl. 12(1) : 31.

Primrose S.B. 1979. Ethylene and agriculture. The role of microbes. J. Appl. Bact. 46 : 1-25.

Prince A.L., Toth S.J., Blair A.W. and Bear F.E. 1941. Forty-year studies of nitrogen fertilizers. Soil Sci. 52 : 247-261.

Quillang R.R. 1981. Effect of rate and date of incorporating ipil-ipil leaves on grain sorghum. M.Sc. Thesis, University of Philippines, Los Baños.

Quintana J.O. 1987. Evaluation of two procedures for screening legume green manures as nitrogen sources to succeeding corn. PhD Thesis. Cornell Univ., Ithaca, NY.

Rabindra B., Naidu B.S., Devi T.G. and Gowda S.N.S. 1989. *Sesbania rostrata* - a low-cost source of N for rice. Int. Rice Res. Newsl. 14(2) : 29.

Raheja P.C. 1952. Why, where, when and how to green manure? Indian Fmg 2(2) : 28-29.

Rai K.D. 1966. Effect of green manuring and fallowing on soil nitrogen and organic carbon and on the succeeding cotton crop in the coastal plain of Sudan. J. Indian Soc. Soil Sci. 14 : 1-8.

Rains D.W. and Talley S.N. 1978. Use of azolla as a source of nitrogen for temperate zone rice culture. In: Proc. Second Rev. Meeting INPUTS Project, East West Center Resources Systems Institute, Honolulu, Hawaii. pp. 167-174.

Rains D.W. and Talley S.N. 1979. Uses of azolla in North America. In : Nitrogen and rice, pp. 417-431. Int. Rice Res. Inst., Los Baños, Philippines.

Rakotonaivo G., Madagascar R.D. and Schramm M. 1988. Effect of azolla green manure on rice yield. Int. Rice Res. Newsl. 13(4) : 29.

Ram D.N. and Zwerman P.J. 1960. Influence of management systems and cover crops on soil physical conditions. Agron. J. 52 : 473-476.

Ramaswami P.A. and Raj D. 1973. Effect of green manure and nutrient applications on the changes in soil microbial populations. Madras Agric. J., 60 : 995-1000.

Ramaswamy S., Dawood A.S. and Chinnaswami K.N. 1988. Organic and inorganic N effect on rice. Int. Rice Res. Newsl. 13(5) : 28.

Rao D. and Mikkelsen D.S. 1977. Effect of acetic, propionic and butyric acids on young rice seedlings growth. Agron. J. 69 : 923-928.

Rao D.L.N. and Batra L. 1983. Ammonia volatilization from applied nitrogen in alkali soils. Plant Soil 70 : 219-228.

Rao W.V.B.S. and Ghosh A.B. 1952. Green manuring. Sci. Cult. 18 : 170-173.

Reddi S.N., Rao G.P., Rao Y.Y. and Reddi G.H. 1972. Note on the effect of green leaf manuring with and without fertilizers on the growth and yield of IR 20 rice. Indian J. Agric. Res. 6 : 67-69.

Reddy K.C., Soffes A.R. and Prine G.M. 1986. Tropical legumes for green manure. 1. Nitrogen production and the effects on succeeding crop yields. Agron. J. 78 : 1-4.

Rekhi R.S. and Meelu O.P. 1983. Effect of complementary use of mung straw and inorganic fertilizer N on the nitrogen availablity and yield of rice. Oryza 20 : 125-129.

Relwani L.L. and Ganguly B.D. 1958. Effect of green manuring in conjunction with fertilizers on paddy yield. Indian J. Agric. Sci. 29 : 1-13.

Rennie D.A., Truog E. and Allen O.N. 1954. Soil aggregation as influenced by microbial gums, level of fertility and kind of crop. Soil Sci. Soc. Am. Proc. 18 : 399-403.

Rennie R.J., Rennie D.A., Siripaibool C., Chaiwanakupt P., Boonkerd N. and Snitwongse P. 1988. N_2 fixation in Thai soybeans: effect of tillage and inoculation on ^{15}N-determined N_2 fixation in recommended cultivars and advanced breeding lines. Plant Soil 112:183-193.

Rika I.K., Nitis I.M. and Humphreys L.R. 1981. Effects of stocking rate on cattle growth, pasture production and coconut yield in Bali. Trop. Grassland 15(3):149-157.

Rinaudo G., Alazard D. and Moudiongui A. 1988. Stem-nodulating legumes as green manure for rice in West Africa. In: Green manure in rice farming, pp. 97-109. Int. Rice Res. Inst., Los Baños, Philippines.

Rinaudo G., Dreyfus B. and Dommergues Y.R. 1983. *Sesbania rostrata* green manure and the nitrogen content of rice crop and soil. Soil Biol. Biochem. 15 : 111-113.

Roger P.A. and Watanabe I. 1986. Technologies for utilizing biological nitrogen fixation in wetland rice: Potentialities, current usage and limiting factors. Fert. Res. 9 : 39-77.

Rosecrance R.C. and Kuo W. 1989. Maize yields from an alley cropping experiment with nine tree species in Hawaii. Nitrogen Fixing Tree Research Reports 7:36-37.

Roy A.C., Wanki S.B.C. and Takow J.A. 1988. Use of green manure in rice farming systems in West and North-west Cameroon. In: Green manure in rice farming, pp. 333-341. Int. Rice Res. Inst., Los Baños, Philippines.

Sadana U.S. and Bajwa M.S. 1985. Manganese equilibrium in submerged sodic soils as influenced by application of gypsum and green manuring. J. Agric. Sci., Camb. 104 : 257-261.

Sadana U.S. and Bajwa M.S. 1986. Effect of gypsum and green manuring on electrochemical and chemical changes in submerged sodic soils. Oryza 23 : 89-95.

Sahu B.N. 1965. Management of lateritic soils of Orissa for increased crop production - a review. Indian J. Agron. 10 : 29-42.

Sahu B.N. and Nayak B.C. 1971. Soil fertility investigation under continuous application of ammonium sulphate alone and in combination with the organic manure in Bhubaneswar long-term fertility trial. In: Proceedings of Int. Symp. on Soil fertility evaluation, pp. 873-879. Indian Soc. Soil Sci., New Delhi.

Saint Macury H., Marqueses E.A., Torres R.O. and Morris R.A. 1985. Effect of flooding on growth and N^2 fixation of two *Sesbania* species. Philipp. J. Crop Sci. 10 : 17-20.

Salam M.A., Hameed S.M.S., Sivaprasad P., Tajuddin E. and Thomas Y. 1989. Performanace of *Sesbania rostrata* in acid soil. Int. Rice Res. Newsl. 14(4) : 33-34.

San Pascual M.S. 1982. Management and utilization of stylo (*Stylosanthes guyanensis* (Aubl. Sw.) as green manure for green sorghum (*Sorghum bicolor* L. Moench). M.S. Thesis, University of Philippines, Los Baños, Philippines.

Sanginga N., Mulongoy K. and Ayanaba A. 1988a. Response of *Leucaeana/Rhizobium* symbiosis to mineral nutrients in south western Nigeria. Plant Soil 112:121-127.

Sanginga N., Mulongoy K. and Ayanaba A. 1988b. Nodulation and growth of *Leucaeana leucocephala* (Lam.) de Wit as affected by inoculation and nitrogen fertilizer. Plant Soil 112:129-135.

Santra G.H., Das D.K. and Mandal L.N. 1988. Loss of nitrogen through ammonia volatilization from flooded rice fields. J. Indian Soc. Soil Sci. 36 : 652-659.

Sanyasi Raju N. 1952. The role of organic manures and inorganic fertilizers in soil fertility. Madras Agric. J. 39 : 130-147.

Sanyasi Raju N. and Govinda Iyer T.A. 1955. Reclamation of alkaline lands in the Cauvery Mettur Project Area. Proc. Natn. Acad. Sci., India 24 A : 606-610.

Sarvanan A., Velu V. and Ramanathan K.M. 1988. Effect of sources and methods of nitrogen application on volatilization loss of ammonia and yield of rice under submerged soils of Cauvery delta, India. Oryza 25 : 143-148.

Satapathy K.B. and Singh P.K. 1985. J. Aquat. Plant Mangement. 23 : 40-45 (c.f. Lumpkin, T.A., 1987 In : Symbiotic nitrogen fixation technology, pp. 55-94, Marcel Dekkar Inc., New York).

Satyanarayana K.V.S., Chibber R.K. and Hadimani A.S. 1961. Relative effect of chemical amendments and *Argemone mexicana* in reclamation of saline and alkali soils. Proc. 48th Indian Sci. Congr. 3 : 125-128.

Sen S. and Rao W.V.B.S. 1953. Phosphate fertilization of legumes. Indian Counc. Agric. Res. (ICAR). Ser. No. 3.

Sethi R.L., Ramiah K. and Abraham T.P. 1952. Manuring of rice in india. Bull 38. Indian Council Agric. Res., New Delhi.

Sharma B.D. and Katyal J.C. 1982. Changes in DTPA-iron and management of iron chlorosis in rice nurseries. Plant Soil 69 : 123-126.

Sharma R.C., Govindakrishnan P.M., Singh R.P. and Sharma H.C. 1988. Effects of farmyard manure and green manures on crop yields and nitrogen needs of potato-based cropping system in Punjab. J.agric. Sci., Camb. 110 : 499-504.

Sharma A.R. and Mittra B.N. 1988. Effect of green manuring and mineral fertilizer on growth and yield of crops in rice-based cropping on lateritic soil. J. agric. Sci., Camb. 110 : 605-608.

Sharma R.C. and Sharma H.C. 1988. Usefulness of organic manures and their nitrogen fertilizer equivalents. J. Agric. Sci., Camb. 111 : 193-195.

Shetty K.S. 1975. Reclamation of saline alkali soils with gypsum, pressmud and zinc sulphate. Indian J. Agric. Chem. 8 : 253-256.

Shi S., Lin X. and Wen Q. 1981. Decomposition of plant materials in relation to their chemical composition in paddy soil. In : Proc. Symp. on Paddy Soil, pp. 306-310. Inst. of Soil Sci., Academia Sinica.

Shinde N.K. and Sen S. 1958. Phosphate manuring of legumes. Indian J. Agron. 3 : 89-98.

Shirwal A.S. and Deshpande P.B. 1977. Reclamation of salt-affected soils in Karnataka. Curr. Res. 6 : 127-129.

Shukla G., Pandey P.C., Bisht P.S. and Lal P. 1989. Economy in combining fertilizer N with green manure in lowland rice. Int. Rice Res. Newsl. 14(4) : 31.

Siagian T.H. and Mabbayad B.B. 1980. Soil properties and corn performance as affected by Leucaena leaves applied as N fertilizer at different rates and by different methods. Philipp. J. Crop. Sci. 5 : 53-57.

Siddiqui M.A., Aslam M., Hayat M.Y. and Sandhu G.R. 1985. Nodulation studies on *Sesbania sesban* (L) Merr. 2. Green manuring for wheat. Pakistan J. Sci. Indus. Res. 28 : 407-411.

Singh A. 1962. Studies on the modus operandi of green manures in tropical climates, Indian J. Agron. 7 : 69-79.

Singh A. 1965. Responses of sugarcane to sunn green manuring in India. Expl Agric. 1 : 209-214.

Singh A. 1967. Long-term effects of green manures in subtropics. Indian J. Agric. Sci. 37 : 226-233.

Singh A.L. and Singh P.K. 1987. The use of *Azolla pinnata* isolates as organic N sources for lowland rice (*Oryza sativa*). Expl Agric. 23 : 159-166.

Singh A.L. and Singh P.K. 1989. A comparison of the use of azolla and blue green algae bio-fertilizers with green manuring, organic manuring and urea in transplanted and direct-seeded rice. Expl Agric. 25 : 485-491.

Singh B. 1990. Quantification of dinitrogen fixed by dhaincha (*Sesbania* spp.) M.Sc. Thesis, Punjab Agric. Univ., Ludhiana, India.

Singh B. and Brar S.P.S. 1985. Effect of organic manures and N on grain yield and soil properties in a maize-wheat rotation. J. Res. (PAU) 22 : 243-252.

Singh B.B. and Jones J.P. 1976. Phosphorus sorption and desorption characteristics of soil as affected by organic residue. Soil Sci. Soc. Am. Proc. 40 : 389-394.

Singh C. and Verma S.S. 1969. Long-range effect of green manuring on soil fertility and wheat yields on black cotton soils under rainfed conditions. Indian J. Agron. 14 : 159-164.

Singh M.P. and Sinha S.K. 1964. Studies on green manuring of wheat in Bilhar. III. Optimum dose of green matter. Indian J. Agron. 9 : 138 -143.

Singh N.T. 1969. Changes in sodic soils incubated under saturated environments. Soil Sci. Pl. Nutr. 15 : 156-160.

Singh N.T. 1974. Physico-chemical changes in sodic soils incubated at saturation. Plant and Soil 40 : 303-311.

Singh N.T. 1984. Green manure as source of nurients in rice production. Organic matter and rice, pp. 229-238. Int. Rice Res. Inst. Los Baños, Philippines.

Singh N.T., Singh R. and Vig A.C. 1981a. Yield and water expenses of cowpea, clusterbean and *Sesbania* as summer green manures in semi-arid regions of Punjab. Indian J. Agric. Sci. 56 : 417-421.

Singh N.T., Verma S.M. and Josan A.S. 1975. Direct and residual effect of green manures and other organic residues on soil aggregation and potato yield. J. Indian Soc. Soil Sci. 23 : 259-262.

Singh P.K. 1977a. Multiplication and utilization of fern azolla containing nitrogen-fixing algae symbiont; a green manure in rice cultivation. Il Riso 26 : 125-137.

Singh P.K. 1977b. Azolla plants as fertilizers and feed. Indian Fmg 27(1) : 19-22.

Singh P.K. 1979. Effect of *Azolla* on the yield of paddy with and without application of N fertilizer. Curr. Sci. 46(8) : 642-644.

Singh P.K. 1982. *Azolla* as an organic nitrogen fertilizer for medium and lowland rice. pp. 236-242. Review of Soil Research in India. Part I. Trans. 12th Int. Congress Soil Sci., New Delhi, India.

Singh P.K., Panigrahi B.C. and Satapathy K.B. 1981b. Comparative efficiency of azolla, blue-green algae and other organic manures in relation to N and P availability in a flooded rice soil. Plant Soil 62 : 35-44.

Singh R., Vig A.C. and Singh N.T. 1982. Nitrogen substitution with green-manures in maize-wheat rotation. Indian J. Agron. 27 : 371-376.

Singh R.G. 1971. Prospectus of utilizing wild legumes as green manures in paddy-wheat rotation. Allahabad Fmg 45 : 479-495.

Singh R.P. and Das S.K. 1984. Nitrogen management in cropping system with particular reference to rainfed lands of India. Part A of Project Bull. 8, ACIRPDA, Hyderabad.

Singh S. 1959. Studies on the cost of reclamation of kallar (alkali lands). Rep. Indian Council Agric. Res. Scheme, 1958-59.

Singh S. and Lamba P.S. 1971. Agronomic studies on cowpeas FS-68. I. Effect of soil moisture regimes, seed rates and levels of phosphorus on growth characters and yield. J. Res. Haryana Agric. Univ. Hissar 3 : 1-7.

Singh S. and Rai R.N. 1973. Effect of soil, superphosphate and age at burial of legumes on the changes in inorganic and organic phosphorus during their decomposition. J. Indian Soc. Soil Sci. 21 : 271-276.

Singh S. and Rai R.N. 1974. Effect of salinity and alkalinity on nitrogen fixation by *Sesbania aculeata* and *Melilotus alba* in presence and absence of superphosphate. Proc. Indian Natl Sci. Acad. Part B, 39 : 576-581.

Singh U.B. 1961. After-effects of green manure crops on uptake of nitrogen and phosphorus by wheat. Indian J. Agron. 6 : 98-104.

Singhabutra N., Arunin S. and Anuluxtipan Y. 1987. Experiment on two rhizobium strains for inoculation into *Sesbania* spp. Use as a green manure on the reclamation of saline soil. Paper presented at the 25th Annual Technical Meeting, 2-6 Feb., Kasetsart University, Bangkok.

Sinha A. 1982. Effect of water stress, salinity and alkalinity on seed germination of *Sesbania aegyptiaca*. Geobios (Jodhpur) 9 : 63-65.

Smith A.M. 1976. Ethylene in soil biology. Ann. Rev. Phytophathol. 14 : 53-73.

Smith M.S., Frye W.W. and Varco J.J. 1987. Legume winter cover crops. Adv. Soil Sci. 7:95-140.

Smyth T.J., Cravo M.S. and Melgar R.J. 1991. Nitrogen supplied to corn by legumes in a central Amazon Oxisol. Trop. Agric. (Trinidad) 68:366-372.

Somani L.L. and Saxena S.N. 1981. The effects of organic and inorganic amendments on the microflora and crop growth in calcareous saline-alkali soil. Pedobiologia 21 : 191-201.

Sowden F.J. and Atkinson A.J. 1968. Effect of long-term annual additions of various organic amendments on the organic matter of a clay and sand. Can. J. Soil Sci. 48 : 323-330.

Srivastava S.C. and Pandit S.N. 1969. Relative role of sunnhemp tops and roots in contributing to the green manuring benefit to sugarcane. Indian J. Agric. Sci. 38 : 338-342.

Staker E.V. 1958. Green manure crops in rotation to paddy production in South-East Asia. Int. Rice Comm. Newsl. (Bangkok) 7(4) : 1-20.

Stickler F.C., Sharder W.D. and Johnson I.J. 1959. Comparative value of legume and fertilizer nitrogen for corn production. Agron. J. 51 : 157-160.

Su N. 1983. Country reports-China. In: Recycling of organic matter in Asia for fertilizer use, pp 91-111. Asian Productivity Organization, Tokyo.

Subba Rao N.S. 1988. Microbiological aspects of green manure in lowland rice soils. In: Green Manure in Rice Farming. Int. Rice Res. Inst, Los Baños, Philippines.

Subbiah B.V. and Mannikar N.D. 1964. Selection of green manure crops for the uptake of subsoil phosphorus - studies with P^{32}. Indian J. Agric. Sci. 34 : 21-27.

Subudhi B.P.R. and Singh P.K. 1983. *Azolla pinnata* as a biofertilizer for rice. Indian J. Agric. Sci. 53 : 320-324.

Swaminathan K. and Singh M. 1960. Value of growing kharif legumes with or without phosphate fertilizers in influencing potato crop. Indian Potato J. 2 : 83-93.

Swarup A. 1986. Effect of pretransplanting submergence and green manure on yield and sodic soil improvement. Int. Rice. Res. Newsl. 11(5) : 39.

Swarup A. 1987. Effect of presubmergence and green manuring (*Sesbania aculeata*) on nutrition and yield of wetland rice (*Oryza sativa* L.) on a sodic soil. Biol. Fertil. Soils 5 : 203-208.

Swarup A. 1988. Effect of *Sesbania bispinosa* decomposition time and sodicity on rice yield. Int. Rice Res. Newsl. 13(6) : 28-29.

Swasdee P., Stangtein J. and Na Nakorn T. 1976. Long-term effect of green manure crop on yield as compared to chemical fertilizer. Summary report on the use of organic fertilizer. Rice Division, Dept. Agric, Ministry of Agriculture and Coop., Thailand.

Tajuddin I., Chin S.L. and Pushparajah E. 1980. Proc. Conf. on Legumes in Tropics, 1979. Univ. Pertanian, Malaysia (c.f. Pushparajah, E. 1982, Trans. 12th Int. Congr, Soil Sci. 2: 189-197).

Talley S.N. and Rains D.W. 1980a. *Azolla filiculoides* Lam. as a fallow-season green manure for rice in a temperate climate. Agron. J. 72 : 11-18.

Talley S.N. and Rains D.W. 1980b. Azolla as a nitrogen source for temperate rice. In: Nitrogen fixation. Vol. II, pp. 311-320. (W.E. Newton and W.H. Orme-Johnson, eds), University Park Press, Baltimore.

Talley S.N., Talley B.T. and Rains D.W. 1977. Nitrogen fixation by azolla in rice fields. In: Genetic engineering in nitrogen fixation, pp. 259-281. (Alexander Hollaender ed.). Plenum Publishing Corp., New York.

Tan K.H., Pushparajah E., Shepherd R. and Teoh C.H. 1976. Proc. Rub. Res. Inst. Malaysia Planter's Conf. 1976, Kuala Lumpur Malaysia (c.f. Pushparajah, E., 1982, Trans. 12th Int. Congr. Soil Sci. 2 : 189-197).

Tan Y.P. and Ng S.K. 1972. Proc. Conf. Fertility and Chemistry of Tropical soils, Malaysian Soc. Soil Sci., Kuala Lumpur, Malaysia, pp. 50-59 (c.f. Pushparajah, E., 1982, Trans. 12th Int. Congr, Soil Sci. 2 : 189-197).

Tejwani K.G., Srinivasan V. and Mistry M.S. 1966. Effect of cover-cum-green manure crop of sunn hemp on soil and water conservation in bidi tobacco fields of Gujrat. Indian J. Agron. 11 : 324-328.

ten Have H. 1959. *Crotalaria quinquefolia* a promising green manure for the rice culture in Surinam. Landbouw 7(2) : 39-50.

ten Holte L. and Van Keulen H. 1989. Effects of white and red clover as a green manure crop in growth, yield and nitrogen response of sugar beet and potatoes. In: Legumes in farming systems, pp. 16-24. (P. Plancquaert and R. Haggar, eds) Kluwer Academic Publications, Dordrecht.

Thind H.S. and Chahal D.S. 1983. Iron equilibria in submerged soils as influenced by green manuring and iron application. J. agric. Sci., Camb. 101 : 207-221.

Thind H.S. and Chahal D.S. 1987. Effect of green manuring (*Sesbania aculeata*) on zinc equilibria in submerged calcareous and non-calcareous soils. Biol. Fertil. Soils 3 : 179-182.

Thomas GV. and Shantaram M.V. 1984. *In situ* cultivation and incorporation of green manure legumes in coconut basins. Plant Soil 80 : 373-380.

Thompson L.M., Black C.A. and Zoelluer, J.A. 1954. Occurrence and mineralization of organic P in soil with particular reference to association with N, C and pH. Soil Sci. 77 : 185-196.

Timsina J. 1981. Effect of indeterminate cowpea (*Vigna unguiculata* L. Walp.) varieties on the succeeding crop of dry seeded rice. M.S. Thesis, Univ. Philippines, Los Baños, Philippines.

Tirol-Padre A. and Ladha J.K. 1990. Effect of planting method and optimum seeding rate on biomass production and nitrogen fixation in *Sesbania rostrata*. Int. Rice Res. Newsl. 15(6):15.

Tiwari K.N., Tiwari S.P. and Pathak A.N. 1980. Studies on green manuring of rice in double-cropping system in a partially reclaimed saline-sodic soil. Indian J. Agron. 25 : 136-145.

Touchton J.T., Rickerl D.H., Walker R.H. and Snipes, C.E. 1984. Winter legumes as a nitrogen source for no-tillage cotton. Soil Tillage Res. 4 : 391-401.

Tsai D.C., Chao, J.C. and Chang L.L. 1962. Studies on the propagation and utilization of azolla, a green manure in paddy fields. Soil Sci. Bull. 4 (China).

Tusneem H.E. and Patrick W.H. Jr. 1971. Nitrogen transformations in waterloggged soils. Bull. No. 657, Louisiana State Univ.

Uppal H.L. 1955. Green manuring with special reference to *Sesbania aculeata* for treatment of alkaline soils. Indian J. Agric. Sci. 25 : 211-235.

Uppal H.L., Agarwal R.R. and Kibe M.M. 1961. Reclamation of saline and alkali lands. Farm Bull. 66 : 1-30. Farm Information Unit, Directorate of Extension, Ministry of Food and Agric., New Delhi.

Utomo M. 1986. Role of legume cover crops in no-tillage and conventional tillage corn production, Ph. D. Thesis, University of Kentucky, Lexington.

Vachhani M.V. and Murty, K.S. 1964. Green manuring for rice. Indian Council Agr. Res., New Delhi, Res. Rep. Ser. No. 17. p.50.

Varco J.J. 1986. Tillage effects on transformation of legume and fertilizer nitrogen and crop recovery of residue nitrogen. Ph.D. Thesis, University of Kentucky, Lexington.

Varco J.J., Frye W.W., Smith M.S. and Grove J.H. 1987. Legume nitrogen tranformation and recovery by corn as influenced by tillage. In: The role of legumes in conservation tillage systems. pp. 40. (J.F. Power ed.) Soil Conservation Society of America.

Venkatakrishnan S. 1980. Mineralization of green manure (*Sesbania aculeata* Pers.) nitrogen in sodic and reclaimed soils under flooded conditions. Plant Soil 54 : 149-152.

Venkateswarlu J. 1987. Efficient resource management systems for drylands of India. Adv. Soil Sci. 7 : 166-221.

Ventura W. and Watanabe I. 1991. Azolla and sesbania: organic fertilizers. In: The Philippine Environment: Opportunities in Conservation and Rehabilitation. The Phil. Futuristic Society, Manila. pp. 171-178.

Ventura W., Mascarina G.B., Furoc R.E. and Watanabe I. 1987. Azolla and sesbania: organic biofertilizers. Philipp. J. Crop Sci. 12:S39.

Ventura W., Mascasins G.B., Furoc R.E. and Watanabe I. 1987. Azolla and sesbania as biofertilizers for lowland rice. Philipp. J. Crop. Sci. 12 : 61-69.

Verma H.N., Sandhu K.S. and Sarora G.S. 1990. Moisture conservation and fertilizer management in submontane Punjab. Prog. Fmg (PAU) 26(8) : 17-18.

Visperas R.M., Furoc R.E., Morris R.A., Vergara B.S. and Patena G. 1987. Flowering response of *Sesbania rostrata* to photoperiod. Philipp. J. Crop Sci. 12 : 147-149.

Vlek P.L.G., Fillery I.R.P. and Burford J.R. 1981. Accession, transformation and loss of nitrogen in soils of the arid region. Plant Soil 58 : 133-175.

Vo Minh Kha and Tran Quang Thuyet. 1970. Beo Hoa Bau (Azolla). Nha Xuat Ban Nong Thon. Hanoi (Viet Nam). 174 pp.

Wagger M.G. 1989. Cover-crop management and nitrogen rate in relation to growth and yield of no-till corn. Agron. J. 81 : 533-538.

Walunjkar W.G., Singh A.N. and Balagopal K. 1968. Green manuring in black cotton soils with flue cured tobacco. Indian J. Agron. 13 : 57-63.

Wang T.S.C., Cheng S.Y. and Tung H. 1967. Dynamics of soil acids. Soil Sci. 104 : 138-144.

Warman P.R. 1980. The basics of green manuring. Macdonald J. 41(1) : 3-6.

Watanabe I. 1984. Use of green manures in Northeast Asia, In: Organic matter and rice, pp. 229-234. International Rice Research Institute, Los Baños, Philippines.

Watanabe I., Berja N.S. and Alimagno V.B. 1977. Utilization of the Azolla-Anabaena complex as a nitrogen fertilizer for rice. Int. Rice Res. Inst. Res. Pap. Ser. 11.

Watanabe I. and Liu C. 1990. Improvement of nitrogen-fixing systems and their integration into sustainable rice farming. 14th Int. Congr. Soil Sci. 3 : 134-138.

Watanabe I., Zhi-Baike N.S., Espinas C.R., Ito O. and Subudhi B.P.R. 1981. Azolla - Anabaena complex and its use in rice culture. Int. Rice. Res. Inst. Res. Pap. Ser. 69.

Weerakoon W.L. 1983. Country reports from Sri Lanka. In: Recycling organic matter in Asia for fertilizer use, pp. 197-216. Asian Productivity Organization, Tokyo.

Weeraratna C.S. 1979. Pattern of N release during decomposition of some green manures, in a tropical alluvial soil. Plant Soil 53 : 287-294.

Wei W.X., Jin G.Y. and Zhang N. 1986. Preliminary report on azolla hybridization studies. Bull. Fujian Acad. Agric. Sci. 1 : 73-79 (Chinese).

Welch C.D., Nelson W.L. and Krantz B.A. 1950. Effect of winter cover crops on soil properties and yields in a cotton-corn and in a cotton-peanut rotation. Soil Sci. Soc. Am. Proc. 15 : 229-234.

Wen Q. 1984. Utilization of organic materials in rice production in China. In: Organic Matter and Rice, pp. 45-56. Int. Rice Res. Inst., Los Baños, Philippines.

Wen. Q. and Yu T. 1988. Effect of green manure on physiochemical properties of irrigated rice soils. In: Green manure in rice farming, pp. 275-288. Int. Rice Res. Inst., Los Baños, Philippines.

Westcott M.P. and Mikkelsen D.S. 1987. Comparison of organic and inorganic nitrogen sources for rice. Agron. J. 79: 937-943.

Westcott M.P. and Mikkelsen D.S. 1988. Effect of green manure in rice soil fertility in the United States. In: Green Manure in Rice Farming, pp. 257-274. Int. Rice Res. Inst., Los Baños, Philippines.

Whyte R.O., Nilsson-Leissner G. and Trumble H.C. 1953. Legumes in agriculture. FAO Agric. Stud. 21. FAO, Rome.

Williams W.A. and Finfrock D.C. 1962. Effect of placement and time of incorporation of vetch on rice yields. Agron. J. 54 : 547-549.

Williams W.A., Finfrock D.C., Davis L.L. and Mikkelsen D.S. 1957. Green manuring and crop residue management in rice production. Soil Sci. Soc. Am. Proc. 21 : 412-415.

Williams W.A., Morre M.D. and Rickman J.E. 1972. Burning vs. incorporation of rice crop residues. Agron. J. 64 : 467-468.

Wilson G.F., Lal R. and Okiybo B.N. 1982. Effects of clover crop on soil structure and on yield of subsequent arable crops grown under strip tillage on an eroded alfisol. Soil Tillage Res. 2 : 233-250.

Wilson G.F. and Kang B.T. 1981. Developing stable and productive cropping systems for the humid tropics. In: Biological husbandry. A scientific approach to organic farming, (B. Stonehouse ed.). Butterworth, London.

Wisniewski A.J., Soloman M. and Smith J.B. 1958. Restoration of soil structure with redtop and other sod crops. Soil Sci, Soc. Am, Proc. 22 : 320-322.

Worshom A.D. 1986. No-tillage research update - North Carolina. In: Southern Region. No-tillage Agriculture - Principles and Practices. Phillips R.E. (ed.). Van Nostrand Reinhold, New York.

Xiao S. 1980. Effect of increased production by its different multiple cropping and crop rotation systems in double-cropped rice field in winter and its influence on soil fertility. Sci. Agric. Sin. 2 : 59-66.

Yaacob O. and Blair G.J. 1981. Effect of legume cropping and organic matter accumulation on the infiltration rate and structural stability of a granite soil under a simulated tropical environment. Plant Soil 60 : 11-20.

Yadav J.S.P. 1975. Reclamation of alkali soils. Indian Fmg 25(5) : 21-22, 30.

Yadav J.S.P. and Agarwal R.R. 1959. Dynamics of soil changes in the reclamation of saline-alkali soils of the Indo-Gangetic alluvium. J. Indian Soc. Soil Sci. 7 : 213-222.

Yadav J.S.P. and Agarwal R.R. 1961. A comparative study on the effectiveness of gypsum and dhaincha (Sesbania aculeata) in the reclamation of a saline-sodic soil. J. Indian Soc. Soil. Sci. 9 : 151-156.

Yadvinder-Singh, Bijay-Singh, Khind C.S. and Meelu O.P. 1988a. Response of flooded rice to green manure. International Rice Research Newsl. 13(4):23-24.

Yadvinder-Singh, Bijay-Singh, Maskina M.S. and Meelu O.P. 1988b. Effect of organic manure, crop residues and green manure (*Sesbania aculeata*) on nitrogen and phosphorus transformations in sandy loam soil at field capacity and waterlogged conditions. Biol. Fertil. Soils 6 : 183-187.

Yadvinder-Singh, Bijay-Singh, Meelu O.P. and Maskina M.S. 1990. Nitrogen equivalence of green manure for wetland rice on coarse-textured soils. Int. Rice Res. Newsl. 15(1) : 23.

Yamazaki K. 1957. Renge rice culture. Toyama Agric. Technol. 4(5) : 1-31.

Yamazaki K. 1959. On milk vetch application in paddy fields. Agric. Hortic. 34(3) : 456.

Yamoah C.E., Agboola A.A., Mulongoy K. 1986a. Decomposition, nitrogen release and weed control by prunings of selected alley-cropping shrubs. Agrofor. Syst. 4 : 239-246.

Yamoah E.F., Agboola A.A. and Wilson G.F. 1986b. Nutrient contribution and maize performance in alley-cropping system. Agrofor. System. 4 : 247-254.

Yatazawa M., Tomomatsu N., Hosoda N. and Nunome. 1980. Nitrogen fixation in *Azolla Anabaena* symbiosis as affected by mineral nutrient status. Soil Sci. Plant Nutr. 26:415-426.

Ye Li-Shu and Wu Can-ling. 1964. Observations on the effect of using hot spring water for azolla overwintering in northern Zhejiang. In: 1964-1974. Collection of Information on Scientific Research. Green Azolla (including *Pistia stratiotes*). Institute of Soil and Fertilizer, Zhejiang Academy of Agricultural Sciences. pp. 46-50.

Yu T. 1985. Physical-chemistry of paddy soils. Science Press, Springer-Verlag, Beijing. Berlin.

Annex 1

List of green manure species

A wide range of leguminous species are used as green-manure crop in various parts of the world. They are usually non-edible herbaceous annuals but include dual-purpose crops, e.g. pulses, from which grains are harvested before ploughing-in the still-green residue. The leaves and green shoots of wild or purpose-grown perennial leguminous trees and shrubs are also used as sources of green manure, and a few examples are given of non-leguminous species. The latter are characterized by easy self-establishment and rapid accumulation of biomass with a lower N content.

For completeness, several species of the floating fern *Azolla* should be mentioned, e.g. *A. pinnata, A. filiculoides, A. microphylla.*

The list is by no means exhaustive and refers mainly to species reported in this publication.

Tropical Green Manures

Annuals

Aeschynomene afraspera (stem-nodulating)
A. crassicaulis (stem-nodulating)
Crotalaria juncea (L.) - sunn hemp
C. spectabilis
C. usaramoensis
Indigofera spicata
I. tinctoria (L.) - indigo
Melilotus alba Medik. - senji
Sesbania aculeata (Wills.) Poir.   =   *S. cannabina* (Retz.) Poir
                                     =   *S. bispinosa* (Jacq.) W.F. Wright
                                         -       dhaincha

S. rostrata (stem-nodulating)
S. speciosa
S. roxburghii
Stylosanthes guianensis (Aubl.) Sw.   =   *S. gracilis* H.B.K. - Brazilian stylo
                                            S. humilis H.B.K. - Townsville stylo

Non-legumes

Argemone mexicana
Eupatorium gladiosa
Ipomoea grandiflora
Tithonia diversifolia A. Gray - Mexican sunflower

Dual-purpose pulse and green-manure crops

Cyamopsis tetragonoloba (L.) Taub. = *C. psoralioides* DC. - guar, clusterbean
Glycine max (L.) Merr. - soybean
Lablab purpureus (L.) Sweet = *Dolichos lablab* (L.) - hyacinth bean, lablab
Phaseolus trilobus = *P. aconitifolius* - pillipesara, moth bean
Vigna radiata (L.) Wilczek var. *aureus* = *Phaseolus aureus* (Roxb.)
                                         = *V. aureus* (Roxb.) Hepp.
                                         - mungbean, green gram
V. radiata var. *mungo* = *P. mungo* L. = *V. mungo* (L.) Hepp. - urd, black gram
V. unguiculata (L.) Walp. - cowpea

Annual/perennial creeping cover crops

Canavalia ensiformis (L.) DC = *Dolichos ensiformis* L. - Jack bean, sword bean
Centrosema pubescens - centro
Calopogonium mucunoides Desv. - calo
Macroptilium atropurpureum (DC.) Urb. - Siratro
Pueraria phaseoloides (Roxb.) Benth. - tropical kudzu

Sub-Tropical/Tropical Green Manures

Annuals

Aeschynomene americana L. - joint vetch
A. indica
Astragalus sinicus L. - milk vetch
Coronilla varia L. - crown vetch
Lupinus angustifolius L. - narrow-leaf lupin
Medicago lupulina L. - trefoil
M. polymorpha L. = *M. denticulata* Willd. - California bur clover
M. sativa L. - alfalfa, lucerne
Mucuna pruriens (L.) DC - velvetbean
Pisum sativum L. - Austrian winter pea
Trifolium alexandrinum L. - berseem clover
T. incarnatum L. - crimson clover
T. pratense L. - red clover
T. repens L. - white clover
Vicia atropurpurea Desv. = *V. benghalensis* L. - purple vetch
V. faba L. - broad bean

V. grandiflora - big-flower vetch
V. sativa L. - common vetch
V. villosa Roth. - hairy vetch

Tropical Trees or Shrubs

Legumes

Cajanus cajan (L.) Millsp. - pigeon pea
Calliandra calothyrsus
Cassia siamea
C. tora
Flemingia congesta
Gliricidia maculata = *G. sepium* = gliricidia, kakuati
Leucaena leucocephala (Lam.) de Wit. = *L. glauca* (L.) Benth. - leucaena, ipil-ipil
Sesbania aegyptiaca = *S. sesban* (L.) Merr. - jantar
S. formosa
S. grandiflora
S. punctata
Tephrosia candida (Roxb.) DC. - white tephrosia
T. pumila
T. purpurea

Non-legumes

Acioa barterii
Adhatoda vasica
Alchornea cordifolia
Melia azadirachta - neem

Annex 2

Biomass and N-accumulation of green manures in Asia, Africa and Latin America

Green manure crop	Age (days)	Dry matter (T/ha)	N-accumulated (kg/ha)	Reference
India				
S. aculeata	60	23.2 (F)	133	Sanyasi Raju (1952)
Sunn hemp	60	30.6 (F)	134	
Cowpea	60	23.2 (F)	74	
Pillipesara	60	25.0 (F)	102	
Sunn hemp	28	2.4	63	Khan & Mathur (1957)
	42	4.4	99	
	56	6.6	140	
Sunn hemp	49	3.4	74	Singh (1961)
Cowpea	49	2.1	49	
Mungbean	49	1.9	42	
Clusterbean	49	1.3	25	
Sunn hemp	42	10.9 (F)	-	Vachhani & Murty (1964)
Sunn hemp	56	16.4 (F)	-	
S. aculeata	42	7.8 (F)	-	
	56	14.5 (F)	-	
Cowpea	42	6.4 (F)	-	
	56	10.2 (F)	-	
Sunn hemp	50	22.1 (F)	98	Ballal *et al*. (1968)
S. aculeata	50	19.3 (F)	81	
Phaseolus mungo	50	13.8 (F)	68	

Green manure crop	Age (days)	Dry matter (T/ha)	N-accumulated (kg/ha)	Reference
P. radiata	50	13.5 (F)	60	
Sunn hemp	60	4.6	78	Bhardwaj *et al.* (1981)
S. aculeata	60	2.9	57	
S. aculeata	28	1.5	38	Singh *et al.* (1981a)
	35	2.2	55	
	42	3.2	80	
	49	3.9	96	
Cowpea	49	4.4	99	Singh *et al.* (1982)
Clusterbean	49	3.2	91	
S. aculeata	49	3.9	84	
S. cannabina	45	3.1	98	Bhardwaj & Dev (1985)
	55	5.3	147	
	65	7.3	163	
S. aculeata	32	0.9	30	Ghai *et al.* (1985)
	52	3.5	99	
	57	5.1	106	
S. aculeata	45	2.5	53	Joseph (1986)
S. aculeata	50	3.8	112	Swarup (1987)
S. aculeata	45	4.7	116	Ghai *et al.* (1988)
S. aculeata	56	3.7	98	Sharma & Mittra (1988)
Sunn hemp	58	4.8	149	
Cowpea	60	6.9	113	Beri *et al.* (1989a)
Sunn hemp	60	5.4	110	
S. aculeata	50	4.7	85	Salam *et al.* (1989)
	60	5.9	131	
Sunn hemp	50	3.4	68	
	60	5.3	110	
S. rostrata	50	5.0	96	
	60	6.1	145	
Sunn hemp	45	3.5	77	Yadvinder-Singh (unpublished data)
	60	6.2	121	

Green manure crop	Age (days)	Dry matter (T/ha)	N-accumulated (kg/ha)	Reference
China				
Milk vetch	flower-ing	22.5-75(F*)	101-338	Bin (1983)
Sesbania sp.		22.5-75 (F)	113-375	
Sunn hemp		15.0-37.5 (F)	60-150	
Common vetch		22.5-45.0 (F)	105-210	
Sweet clover		30.0-60.0 (F)	150-300	
A. indica	30	15	-	Liu (1988)
Japan				
Milk vetch	flower-ing	19.0-37.5 (F)	65-131	Watanabe (1984)
Soybean		11.0-30.0 (F)	64-174	
Medicago denticulata		0.3-5.6 (F)	18-35	
Taiwan				
S. sesban	-		92	Staker (1958)
Sunn hemp	-		89	
Cameroon				
Crotolaria caricia/Sesbania sp.	70-100 (50% flower-ing)	35.0-45.0 (F)	-	Roy *et al.* (1988)
Tephrosia sp.	90	30.0-45.0 (F)	-	
Senegal				
S. rostrata	52	-	267-303	Rinaudo *et al.* (1983) (microplot expt)
A. afraspera/A. nilotica	49	16.0-19.0	423-532	Alazard & Becker (1987) (microplot expt)
Thailand				
S. rostrata	55	-	131	Crozat & Sangchyosawat (1985)
A. indica	55	-	41	
S. rostrata	45	1.5-3.0	62-88	Gines *et al.* (1986)
S. rostrata	61	2.1-5.1	48-116	Herrera *et al.* (1989)

Green manure crop	Age (days)	Dry matter (T/ha)	N-accumulated (kg/ha)	Reference
Philippines				
Sunn hemp	90	3.1	107	Hernandez *et al.* (1957)
Cowpea	90	2.4	112	
Tephrosia candida	105	3.0	139	
Indigofera hirsuta	105	3.5	128	
Mungbean	40	-	86	Morris *et al* (1986a)
Cowpea	45	-	74	
Cowpea	45 DAE	2.4	66	John *et al.* (1989c)
S. cannabina	48	4.9	79	Morris *et al.* (1989)
	60	7.5	198	
Mungbean	48	1.8	34	
S. rostrata	48	3.3	98	
	60	7.0	157	
S. aculeata	60	8.9	199	Meelu *et al.* (1992)
Sunn hemp	60	8.1	143	
Soybean	60	6.4	138	
Cowpea	60	3.3	75	
Pigeon pea	60	3.6	76	
Mungbean	60	3.6	93	
Indigofera tinctoria	60	3.2	84	
S. rostrata (wet season)	56	6.2	159	Manguiat *et al.* (1992)
S. rostrata wet season	59	8.4-11.2	155-194	Becker *et al.* (1990)
dry season	56	4.1-5.4	83-117	
A. afraspera wet season	40	3.7-7.8	155-204	
dry season	56	4.3-7.2	138-149	
S. rostrata wet season	49	11.2-12.4	194-252	Becker *et al.* (1991)
dry season	49	5.0-6.6	103-143	
S. rostrata wet season	44-47		74-79	Ventura *et al.* (1987)
dry season	57		64	

Green manure crop	Age (days)	Dry matter (T/ha)	N-accumulated (kg/ha)	Reference
S. rostrata				
wet season	48		79	Furoc & Morris (1989)
dry season	60		162	
S. rostrata	56	6.2	159	Manguiat *et al*. (1992)
Sri Lanka				
S. sesban	84	4.3	83	Palm *et al*. (1988)
Latin America				
Mucuna (dry season)		8.5	252	Bowen (1987)
Mucuna (wet season)		5.6	182	
Mucuna (dry season)		4.9	117	Quintana (1987)
Zornia (dry season)		2.5	58	
Jack bean (dry season)		5.0	156	
Crotalaria striata (dry season)		10.3	170	
Jack bean (dry season)		10.0	228	Carsky (1989)
Pigeon pea (dry season)		10.4	229	
Jack bean (dry season)		8.9	231	
Calopogonium mucunoides (dry season)		7.3	142	
Mucuna (dry season)		6.8	152	
Kudzu (dry season)		6.5	116	

*F = Fresh matter

WORLD SOIL RESOURCES REPORTS

1. Report of the First Meeting of the Advisory Panel on the Soil Map of the World, Rome, 19-23 June 1961.**
2. Report of the First Meeting on Soil Survey, Correlation and Interpretation for Latin America, Rio de Janeiro, Brazil, 28-31 May 1962**
3. Report of the First Soil Correlation Seminar for Europe, Moscow, USSR, 16-28 July 1962.**
4. Report of the First Soil Correlation Seminar for South and Central Asia, Tashkent, Uzbekistan, USSR, 14 September-2 October 1962.**
5. Report of the Fourth Session of the Working Party on Soil Classification and Survey (Subcommission on Land and Water Use of the European Commission on Agriculture), Lisbon, Portugal, 6-10 March 1963.**
6. Report of the Second Meeting of the Advisory Panel on the Soil Map of the World, Rome, 9-11 July 1963.**
7. Report of the Second Soil Correlation Seminar for Europe, Bucharest, Romania, 29 July-6 August 1963.**
8. Report of the Third Meeting of the Advisory Panel on the Soil Map of the World, Paris, 3 January 1964.**
9. Adequacy of Soil Studies in Paraguay, Bolivia and Peru, November-December 1963.**
10. Report on the Soils of Bolivia, January 1964.**
11. Report on the Soils of Paraguay, January 1964.**
12. Preliminary Definition, Legend and Correlation Table for the Soil Map of the World, Rome, August 1964.**
13. Report of the Fourth Meeting of the Advisory Panel on the Soil Map of the World, Rome, 16-21 May 1964.**
14. Report of the Meeting on the Classification and Correlation of Soils from Volcanic Ash, Tokyo, Japan, 11-27 June 1964.**
15. Report of the First Session of the Working Party on Soil Classification, Survey and Soil Resources of the European Commission on Agriculture, Florence, Italy, 1-3 October 1964.**
16. Detailed Legend for the Third Draft on the Soil Map of South America, June 1965.**
17. Report of the First Meeting on Soil Correlation for North America, Mexico, 1-8 February 1965.**
18. The Soil Resources of Latin America, October 1965.**
19. Report of the Third Correlation Seminar for Europe: Bulgaria, Greece, Romania, Turkey, Yugoslavia, 29 August-22 September 1965.**
20. Report of the Meeting of Rapporteurs, Soil Map of Europe (Scale 1:1 000 000) (Working Party on Soil Classification and Survey of the European Commission on Agriculture), Bonn, Federal Republic of Germany, 29 November-3 December 1965.**
21. Report of the Second Meeting on Soil Survey, Correlation and Interpretation for Latin America, Rio de Janeiro, Brazil, 13-16 July 1965.**
22. Report of the Soil Resources Expedition in Western and Central Brazil, 24 June-9 July 1965.**
23. Bibliography on Soils and Related Sciences for Latin America (1st edition), December 1965.**
24. Report on the Soils of Paraguay (2nd edition), August 1964.**
25. Report of the Soil Correlation Study Tour in Uruguay, Brazil and Argentina, June-August 1964.**
26. Report of the Meeting on Soil Correlation and Soil Resources Appraisal in India, New Delhi, India, 5-15 April 1965.**
27. Report of the Sixth Session of the Working Party on Soil Classification and Survey of the European Commission on Agriculture, Montpellier, France, 7-11 March 1967.**
28. Report of the Second Meeting on Soil Correlation for North America, Winnipeg-Vancouver, Canada, 25 July-5 August 1966.**
29. Report of the Fifth Meeting of the Advisory Panel on the Soil Map of the World, Moscow, USSR, 20-28 August 1966.**
30. Report of the Meeting of the Soil Correlation Committee for South America, Buenos Aires, Argentina, 12-19 December 1966.**
31. Trace Element Problems in Relation to Soil Units in Europe (Working Party on Soil Classification and Survey of the European Commission on Agriculture), Rome, 1967.**
32. Approaches to Soil Classification, 1968.**

33. Definitions of Soil Units for the Soil Map of the World, April 1968.**
34. Soil Map of South America 1:5 000 000, Draft Explanatory Text, November 1968.**
35. Report of a Soil Correlation Study Tour in Sweden and Poland, 27 September-14 October 1968.**
36. Meeting of Rapporteurs, Soil Map of Europe (Scale 1:1 000 000) (Working Party on Soil Classification and Survey of the European Commission on Agriculture), Poitiers, France 21-23 June 1967.**
37. Supplement to Definition of Soil Units for the Soil Map of the World, July 1969.**
38. Seventh Session of the Working Party on Soil Classification and Survey of the European Commission on Agriculture, Varna, Bulgaria, 11-13 September 1969.**
39. A Correlation Study of Red and Yellow Soils in Areas with a Mediterranean Climate.**
40. Report of the Regional Seminar of the Evaluation of Soil Resources in West Africa, Kumasi, Ghana, 14-19 December 1970.**
41. Soil Survey and Soil Fertility Research in Asia and the Far East, New Delhi, 15-20 February 1971.**
42. Report of the Eighth Session of the Working Party on Soil Classification and Survey of the European Commission on Agriculture, Helsinki, Finland, 5-7 July 1971.**
43. Report of the Ninth Session of the Working Party on Soil Classification and Survey of the European Commission on Agriculture, Ghent, Belgium 28-31 August 1973.**
44. First Meeting of the West African Sub-Committee on Soil Correlation for Soil Evaluation and Management, Accra, Ghana, 12-19 June 1972.**
45. Report of the Ad Hoc Expert Consultation on Land Evaluation, Rome, Italy, 6-8 January 1975.**
46. First Meeting of the Eastern African Sub-Committee for Soil Correlation and Land Evaluation, Nairobi, Kenya, 11-16 March 1974.**
47. Second Meeting of the Eastern African Sub-Committee for Soil Correlation and Land Evaluation, Addis Ababa, Ethiopia, 25-30 October 1976.
48. Report on the Agro-Ecological Zones Project, Vol. 1 - Methodology and Results for Africa, 1978. Vol. 2 - Results for Southwest Asia, 1978.
49. Report of an Expert Consultation on Land Evaluation Standards for Rainfed Agriculture, Rome, Italy, 25-28 October 1977.
50. Report of an Expert Consultation on Land Evaluation Criteria for Irrigation, Rome, Italy, 27 February-2 March 1979.
51. Third Meeting of the Eastern African Sub-Committee for Soil Correlation and Land Evaluation, Lusaka, Zambia, 18-30 April 1978.
52. Land Evaluation Guidelines for Rainfed Agriculture, Report of an Expert Consultation, 12-14 December 1979.
53. Fourth Meeting of the West African Sub-Committee for Soil Correlation and Land Evaluation, Banjul, The Gambia, 20-27 October 1979.
54. Fourth Meeting of the Eastern African Sub-Committee for Soil Correlation and Land Evaluation, Arusha, Tanzania, 27 October-4 November 1980.
55. Cinquième réunion du Sous-Comité Ouest et Centre africain de corrélation des sols pour la mise en valeur des terres, Lomé, Togo, 7-12 décembre 1981.
56. Fifth Meeting of the Eastern African Sub-Committee for Soil Correlation and Land Evaluation, Wad Medani, Sudan, 5-10 December 1983.
57. Sixième réunion du Sous-Comité Ouest et Centre Africain de corrélation des sols pour la mise en valeur des terres, Niamey, Niger, 6-12 février 1984.
58. Sixth Meeting of the Eastern African Sub-Committee for Soil Correlation and Land Evaluation, Maseru, Lesotho, 9-18 October 1985.
59. Septième réunion du Sous-Comité Ouest et Centre africain de corrélation des sols pour la mise en valeur des terres, Ouagadougou, Burkina Faso, 10-17 novembre 1985.
60. Revised Legend, Soil Map of the World, FAO-Unesco-ISRIC, 1988. Reprinted 1990.
61. Huitième réunion du Sous-Comité Ouest et Centre africain de corrélation des sols pour la mise en valeur des terres, Yaoundé, Cameroun, 19-28 janvier 1987.
62. Seventh Meeting of the East and Southern African Sub-Committee for Soil Correlation and Evaluation, Gaborone, Botswana, 30 March-8 April 1987.
63. Neuvième réunion du Sous-Comité Ouest et Centre africain de corrélation des sols pour la mise en valeur des terres, Cotonou, Bénin, 14-23 novembre 1988.

64. FAO-ISRIC Soil Database (SDB), 1989.
65. Eighth Meeting of the East and Southern African Sub-Committee for Soil Correlation and Land Evaluation, Harare, Zimbabwe, 9-13 October 1989.
66. World soil resources. An explanatory note on the FAO World Soil Resources Map at 1:25 000 000 scale, 1991.
67. Digitized Soil Map of the World, Volume 1: Africa. Volume 2: North and Central America. Volume 3: Central and South America. Volume 4: Europe and West of the Urals. Volume 5: North East Asia. Volume 6: Near East and Far East. Volume 7: South East Asia and Oceania. Release 1.0, November 1991.
68. Land Use Planning Applications. Proceedings of the FAO Expert Consultation 1990, Rome, 10-14 December 1990.
69. Dixième réunion du Sous-Comité Ouest et Centre africain de corrélation des sols pour la mise en valeur des terres, Bouaké, Odienné, Côte d'Ivoire, Côte d'Ivoire, 5-12 november 1990.
70. Ninth Meeting of the East and Southern African Sub-Committee for Soil Correlation and Land Evaluation, Lilongwe, Malawi, 25 November - 2 December 1991.
71. Agro-ecological land resources assessment for agricultural development planning. A case study of Kenya. Resources data base and land productivity. Main Report. Technical Annex 1: Land resources. Technical Annex 2: Soil erosion and productivity. Technical Annex 3: Agro-climatic and agro-edaphic suitabilities for barley, oat, cowpea, green gram and pigeonpea. Technical Annex 4: Crop productivity. Technical Annex 5: Livestock productivity. Technical Annex 6: Fuelwood productivity. Technical Annex 7: Systems documentation guide to computer programs for land productivity assessments. Technical Annex 8: Crop productivity assessment: results at district level. 1991.
72. Computerized systems of land resources appraisal for agricultural development, 1993.
73. FESLM: an international framework for evaluating sustainable land management, 1993.
74. Global and national soils and terrain digital databases (SOTER), 1993.
75. AEZ in Asia. Proceedings of the Regional Workshop on Agro-ecological Zones Methodology and Applications, Bangkok, Thailand, 17-23 November 1991.
76. Green manuring for soil productivity improvement, 1994.

** Out of print